EMS Textbooks in Mathematics

EMS Textbooks in Mathematics is a series of books aimed at students or professional mathematicians seeking an introduction into a particular field. The individual volumes are intended not only to provide relevant techniques, results, and applications, but also to afford insight into the motivations and ideas behind the theory. Suitably designed exercises help to master the subject and prepare the reader for the study of more advanced and specialized literature.

Markus Stroppel, *Locally Compact Groups*
Peter Kunkel and Volker Mehrmann, *Differential-Algebraic Equations*
Dorothee D. Haroske and Hans Triebel, *Distributions, Sobolev Spaces, Elliptic Equations*
Thomas Timmermann, *An Invitation to Quantum Groups and Duality*
Oleg Bogopolski, *Introduction to Group Theory*
Marek Jarnicki and Peter Pflug, *First Steps in Several Complex Variables: Reinhardt Domains*
Tammo tom Dieck, *Algebraic Topology*
Mauro C. Beltrametti et al., *Lectures on Curves, Surfaces and Projective Varieties*
Wolfgang Woess, *Denumerable Markov Chains*
Eduard Zehnder, *Lectures on Dynamical Systems. Hamiltonian Vector Fields and Symplectic Capacities*
Andrzej Skowroński and Kunio Yamagata, *Frobenius Algebras I. Basic Representation Theory*
Piotr W. Nowak and Guoliang Yu, *Large Scale Geometry*
Joaquim Bruna and Juliá Cufí, *Complex Analysis*
Eduardo Casas-Alvero, *Analytic Projective Geometry*
Fabrice Baudoin, *Diffusion Processes and Stochastic Calculus*
Olivier Lablée, *Spectral Theory in Riemannian Geometry*
Dietmar A. Salamon, *Measure and Integration*
Andrzej Skowroński and Kunio Yamagata, *Frobenius Algebras II. Tilted and Hochschild Extension Algebras*
Jørn Justesen and Tom Høholdt, *A Course In Error-Correcting Codes, Second edition*
Timothée Marquis, *An Introduction to Kac–Moody Groups over Fields*

Bogdan Nica

A Brief Introduction to Spectral Graph Theory

European Mathematical Society

Author:

Bogdan Nica
Department of Mathematics and Statistics
McGill University
805 Sherbrooke St W
Montreal, QC H3A 0B9
Canada

E-mail: bogdan.nica@gmail.com

2010 Mathematics Subject Classification: Primary: 05-01, 05C50; secondary: 05C25, 11T24, 15A42

Key words: Adjacency eigenvalues of graphs, Laplacian eigenvalues of graphs, Cayley graphs, algebraic graphs over finite fields, character sums

ISBN 978-3-03719-188-0

The Swiss National Library lists this publication in The Swiss Book, the Swiss national bibliography, and the detailed bibliographic data are available on the Internet at http://www.helveticat.ch.

Contact address:

European Mathematical Society Publishing House
Seminar for Applied Mathematics
ETH-Zentrum SEW A21
CH-8092 Zürich
Switzerland

Email: info@ems-ph.org
Homepage: www.ems-ph.org

Typeset using the author's T$_E$X files: Alison Durham, Manchester, UK
Printing and binding: Beltz Bad Langensalza GmbH, Bad Langensalza, Germany
∞ Printed on acid free paper
9 8 7 6 5 4 3 2 1

For A.

Contents

Introduction

Spectral graph theory starts by associating matrices to graphs — notably, the adjacency matrix and the Laplacian matrix. The general theme is then, firstly, to compute or estimate the eigenvalues of such matrices, and secondly, to relate the eigenvalues to structural properties of graphs. As it turns out, the spectral perspective is a powerful tool. Some of its loveliest applications concern facts that are, in principle, purely graph theoretic or combinatorial. To give just one example, spectral ideas are a key ingredient in the proof of the so-called friendship theorem: if, in a group of people, any two persons have exactly one common friend, then there is a person who is everybody's friend.

This text is an introduction to spectral graph theory, but it could also be seen as an invitation to algebraic graph theory. On the one hand, there is, of course, the linear algebra that underlies the spectral ideas in graph theory. On the other hand, most of our examples are graphs of algebraic origin. The two recurring sources are Cayley graphs of groups, and graphs built out of finite fields. In the study of such graphs, some further algebraic ingredients — for example, characters — naturally come up.

The table of contents gives, as it should, a good glimpse of where this text is going. Very broadly, the first half is devoted to graphs, finite fields, and how they come together. This part is meant as an appealing and meaningful motivation. It provides a context that frames and fuels much of the second, spectral, half.

Many sections have one or two exercises. They are optional, in the sense that virtually nothing in the main body depends on them. But the exercises are usually of the non-trivial variety, and they should enhance the text in an interesting way. The hope is that the reader will enjoy them. At any rate, solutions are provided at the end of the text.

We assume a basic familiarity with linear algebra, finite fields, and groups, but not necessarily with graph theory. This, again, betrays our algebraic perspective.

Acknowledgments. I would like to thank Péter Csikvári, for thoughtful feedback; Sebastian Cioabă, for several discussions; Jerome Baum, for early help with some pictures; Alain Matthes, for his online gallery of named graphs.

Q_3 = binary strings of length 3

000	⓪
001	①
010	②
011	③
100	④
101	⑤
110	⑥
111	⑦

⓪ : ①, ②, ④
① : ⓪, ③, ⑤
② : ③, ⓪, ⑥
③ : ②, ①, ⑦
④ : ⑤, ⑥, ⓪
⑤ : ④, ⑦, ①
⑥ : ⑦, ④, ②
⑦ : ⑥, ⑤, ③

1

Graphs

We start with some graph-theoretic basics — vocabulary, examples, facts, notation.

1.1 Notions

A *graph* consists of vertices, and edges connecting certain pairs of vertices.

Throughout this text, graphs are *finite* (there are finitely many vertices), *undirected* (edges can be traversed in both directions), and *simple* (there are no loops or multiple edges). Unless otherwise mentioned, graphs are also assumed to be *connected* (any vertex links to any other vertex by a sequence of edges) and *non-trivial* (there are at least three vertices). On a few occasions the singleton graph, ∘, the 'marriage graph', ∘—∘, or disconnected graphs will come up. By and large, however, when we say 'a graph' we mean that the above conditions are fulfilled.

Two vertices that are joined by an edge are said to be *adjacent*, or *neighbours*. When two vertices v and w are adjacent, we write $v \sim w$. The *degree* of a vertex counts the number of its neighbours. A graph is *regular* if all its vertices have the same degree.

A *graph isomorphism* is a bijection between the vertex sets of two graphs such that two vertices in one graph are adjacent if and only if the corresponding two vertices in the other graph are adjacent. Isomorphic graphs are viewed as being the same graph.

Basic examples of regular graphs include the *complete graph K_n*, the *cycle graph C_n*, and the *cube Q_n*. See Figure 1.1. The complete graph K_n has n vertices, with edges connecting any pair of distinct vertices. Hence K_n is regular of degree $n - 1$. The cycle graph C_n has n vertices, and it is regular of degree 2. The cube graph Q_n has the binary strings of length n as vertices, with edges connecting two strings that differ in exactly one slot. Thus Q_n has 2^n vertices, and it is regular of degree n.

Another example of a regular graph is the Petersen graph, a 3-regular graph on 10 vertices pictured in Figure 1.2. A formal description of the Petersen graph runs as follows: the vertices are the 2-element subsets of a 5-element set, and edges represent the relation of being disjoint. The Petersen graph is, in many ways, the smallest interesting graph.

Notable families of non-regular graphs are the path graphs, the star graphs, the wheel graphs, and the windmill graphs — all illustrated in Figure 1.3.

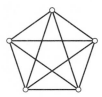 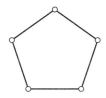

Figure 1.1. Complete graph K_5. Cycle graph C_5. Cube graph Q_3.

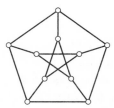 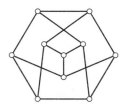 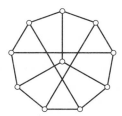

Figure 1.2. Three views of the Petersen graph.

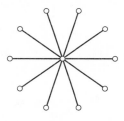 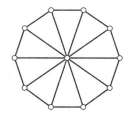 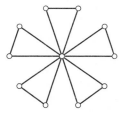

Figure 1.3. Star graph. Wheel graph. Windmill graph. Path graph.

We remark that the marriage graph ∘–∘ is a degenerate case for several of the families mentioned above. From now on we denote it by K_2.

We usually denote a graph by X. We write V and E for the vertex set, respectively the edge set. The two fundamental parameters of a graph are

n : number of vertices,
d : maximal vertex degree.

Our non-triviality assumption means that $n \geq 3$ and $d \geq 2$. If X is regular, then d

is simply the degree of every vertex. In general, the degree is a map on the vertices, $v \mapsto \deg(v)$. We put all this notation to work in the following useful fact.

Proposition 1.1. Let X be a graph. Then the following holds:

$$\sum_{v \in V} \deg(v) = 2|E|.$$

In particular, $dn \geq 2|E|$ with equality if and only if X is regular.

A *path* in a graph connects some vertex v to some other vertex w by a sequence of adjacent vertices $v = v_0 \sim v_1 \sim \cdots \sim v_k = w$. A path is allowed to contain backtracks, that is, steps of the form $u \sim u' \sim u$. The defining property of a connected graph is that any two vertices can be joined by a path. A path from a vertex v to itself is said to be a closed path based at v. A *cycle* is a non-trivial closed path with distinct intermediate vertices. Here, non-triviality means that we rule out empty paths, and back-and-forths across edges.

The *length* of a path is given by the number of edges, counted with multiplicity. An integral-valued *distance* on the vertices of a graph can be defined as follows: the distance $\mathrm{dist}(v, w)$ between two vertices v and w is the minimal length of a path from v to w. So metric concepts such as diameter, and spheres or balls around a vertex, make sense.

Exercise 1.2. A graph on n vertices that contains no 3-cycles has at most $\lfloor n^2/4 \rfloor$ edges.

A *tree* is a graph that has no cycles. For instance, star graphs and path graphs are trees. Two important examples are the trees $T_{d,R}$ and $\tilde{T}_{d,R}$, described as follows. There is a 'root' vertex of degree $d - 1$ in $T_{d,R}$, respectively of degree d in $\tilde{T}_{d,R}$; the pendant vertices lie on a sphere of radius R about the root; the remaining intermediate vertices all have degree d. See Figure 1.4 for an illustration.

By a *pendant* vertex in a graph we mean a vertex having degree 1. Any tree has at least two pendant vertices.

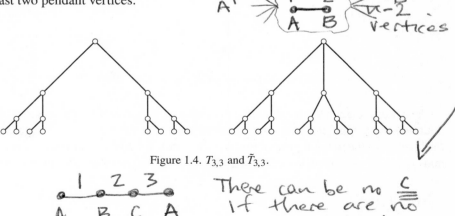

Figure 1.4. $T_{3,3}$ and $\tilde{T}_{3,3}$.

Let X_1 and X_2 be two graphs with vertex sets V_1, respectively V_2. The *product graph* $X_1 \times X_2$ has vertex set $V_1 \times V_2$, and edges defined as follows: $(u_1, u_2) \sim (v_1, v_2)$ if either $u_1 \sim v_1$ and $u_2 = v_2$, or $u_1 = v_1$ and $u_2 \sim v_2$. Let us point out that there are several reasonable ways of defining a product of two graphs. The type of product that we have defined is, however, the only one we will use.

For example, the n-fold product $K_2 \times \cdots \times K_2$ is the cube graph Q_n. Another product we will encounter is $K_n \times K_n$. This is known as the rook's graph, since one can think of $K_n \times K_n$ as describing the possible moves of a rook on an $n \times n$ chessboard.

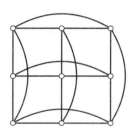 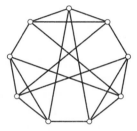

Figure 1.5. Two views of $K_3 \times K_3$.

stopped

How do we tell two graphs apart? Obstructions to graph isomorphism are provided globally by size, and locally by vertex degrees. Such counting criteria are, however, quite naive. For example, they are useless in distinguishing the 3-regular graphs on 8 vertices that are pictured in Figure 1.6.

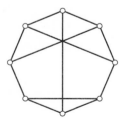 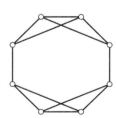 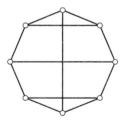

Figure 1.6. Three 3-regular graphs on 8 vertices.

So let us enhance the local information offered by vertex degrees. Instead of just counting the neighbours of a vertex, we consider their structure. Given a graph, the *link graph* (or the *neighbourhood graph*) of a vertex has all its neighbours as vertices, and edges inherited from the ambient graph. A graph isomorphism is link preserving, in the sense that it induces a graph isomorphism between the corresponding link graphs.

As an illustration of this idea, let us consider again the graphs in Figure 1.6, and let us record the pattern of link graphs. The middle graph has link graphs o—o o and o—o—o. The other two graphs have two types of link graphs, o—o o and o o o. The number of vertices having each type is, however, different. In conclusion, the graphs in Figure 1.6 are mutually non-isomorphic.

Exercise 1.3. Show that the regular graph in Figure 1.7 has no non-trivial automorphisms.

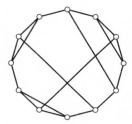

Figure 1.7. The Frucht graph.

Notes. The word 'graph' was coined by Sylvester in 1878, as an abbreviation of 'graphical notation'. This was a well-established term among chemists at the time, and it referred to depictions of molecules in which nodes represented atoms, and edges indicated bonds between them. But the first result of graph-theoretic significance dates back to 1735, and that is Euler's solution to the Königsberg seven-bridge problem.

1.2 Bipartite graphs

A graph is said to be *bipartite* if its vertex set can be partitioned into two subsets, such that no two points belonging to the same subset are connected by an edge. We note that, if it exists, such a bipartition is unique. We often think of the two subsets as consisting of 'white', respectively 'black', vertices.

For example, the cube graph Q_n is bipartite. Indeed, we may partition the binary strings by the weight parity, where the *weight* of a binary string is the number of entries equal to 1 — in other words, the distance to the all-0s string. Also trees are bipartite: the choice of a base vertex defines a partition according to the parity of the distance to the chosen vertex.

The *complete bipartite graph* $K_{m,n}$ is the bipartite counterpart of a complete graph K_n. The vertices of $K_{m,n}$ are two disjoint sets of size m, respectively n, with edges connecting each element of one set to every element of the other set. We might emphasize $K_{n,n}$ for being regular, and $K_{1,n}$ for being the familiar star graph with n pendant vertices.

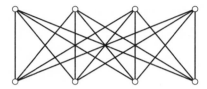

Figure 1.8. Complete bipartite graph $K_{4,4}$.

The complete graph K_n is not bipartite, as it contains 3-cycles. A cycle graph C_n is bipartite if and only if n is even. In fact, bipartiteness can be characterized as follows.

Theorem 1.4. A graph is bipartite if and only if it contains no cycles of odd length.

Proof. If a graph is bipartite, then a path of odd length has its endpoints in different sides of the bi-partition - in particular it cannot be a cycle. For the other direction, pick a vertex u. If all cycles have even length then all closed paths have even length, which in turn implies that lengths of paths from a fixed vertex u to any other vertex v have a well-defined parity. This induces a partition of the vertex set into two types, the 'odd' and the 'even' vertices with respect to u, and there are no edges between vertices of the same type.   □

Exercise 1.5. A graph on n vertices that contains no 3-cycles has $\lfloor n^2/4 \rfloor$ edges. What is the graph?

There is a canonical way of passing from non-bipartite graphs to bipartite ones. The *bipartite double* of a graph X is the graph whose vertex set consists of two disjoint copies, $V_\bullet$ and $V_\circ$, of the vertex set of X, and two vertices $u_\bullet$ and $v_\circ$ are adjacent if and only if u and v are adjacent in X. Thus, we get two edges, $u_\bullet \sim v_\circ$ and $u_\circ \sim v_\bullet$, for each edge $u \sim v$ in X.

For example, the bipartite double of K_4 is depicted in Figure 1.9. It resembles $K_{4,4}$, except that 4 edges given by a black–white pairing have been removed. After unwrapping the tangle, it turns out to be the cube graph Q_3.

As another example, consider the bipartite double of the Petersen graph. This is known as the *Desargues graph*, and it is drawn in Figure 1.10.

The bipartite double of a cycle C_n is the doubled cycle C_{2n} if n is odd, and twice the cycle C_n if n is even. This is an instance of a general phenomenon.

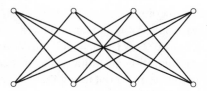

Figure 1.9. Bipartite double of K_4.

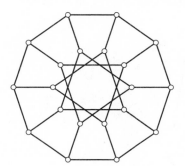 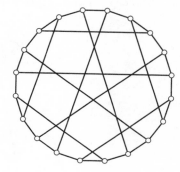

Figure 1.10. Two views of the Desargues graph.

Proposition 1.6. The bipartite double of a graph X is connected if and only if X is non-bipartite.

Proof. A vertex $u_\bullet$ is connected to $v_\bullet$, respectively to $v_\circ$, in the bipartite double of X if and only if u is connected to v in X by a path of even, respectively odd, length. Thus, if the bipartite double is connected, then a path from $u_\bullet$ to $v_\bullet$ and one from $u_\bullet$ to $v_\circ$ yield a closed path of odd length in X, so X is non-bipartite. Conversely, assume that X is non-bipartite, so X contains some cycle of odd length. Pick a vertex u on the cycle. We claim that, in X, we can join u to any other vertex v by a path of even length, as well as by one of odd length. Indeed, take a path p from u to v. Then p and the path p', obtained by first going once around the cycle and then following p, are two paths from u to v of different parities. In the bipartite double, this means that $u_\bullet$ is connected to $v_\bullet$ and to $v_\circ$, no matter what v is. Thus, the bipartite double is connected. □

The upshot is that we will take only bipartite doubles of non-bipartite graphs.

But we can also ask the reverse question: given a bipartite graph, is it the bipartite double of some other graph? A very simple parity obstruction is sometimes effective. We illustrate it on a concrete example.

Example 1.7. A geometric theorem ascribed to Pappus states the following: if A, B, C and A', B', C' are two triples of collinear points, then the triple of intersection points $X = AB' \cap A'B$, $Y = AC' \cap A'C$, $Z = BC' \cap B'C$ are collinear as well. We associate a graph to this configuration, as follows: the vertices are the points and the lines, and edges connect points to lines containing them. The resulting *Pappus graph* is a bipartite 3-regular graph on 18 vertices.

We claim that the Pappus graph is not a bipartite double. For if it were, then it would be the bipartite double of a 3-regular graph on 9 vertices. But this is impossible, since a regular graph cannot have both odd degree and odd size.

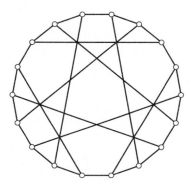

Figure 1.11. The Pappus graph.

This example also introduces the idea of constructing bipartite graphs from geometric configurations, as incidence graphs. The Desargues graph, for example, draws its name from being the incidence graph of the so-called Desargues configuration.

2

Invariants

A graph invariant is some property of a graph, most commonly a number, that is preserved by isomorphisms. There are a great variety of numerical invariants that one can associate to a graph besides the fundamental parameters n (the size) and d (the maximal degree). Among the most important, and the ones we are interested in here, are the chromatic number, the independence number, the diameter, the girth, and the isoperimetric constant. Roughly speaking, the first two measure the freeness, the next two the largeness, and the last one the connectivity of a graph.

2.1 Chromatic number and independence number

The *chromatic number* of a graph is the minimal number of colours needed to paint the vertices in such a way that adjacent vertices have different colours. The *independence number* of a graph is the maximal number of vertices that can be chosen so that no two of them are adjacent. A set of vertices is said to be *independent* if no two vertices are adjacent.

Consider a graph with n vertices. The chromatic number satisfies $2 \leq \mathrm{chr} \leq n$. At the extremes, $\mathrm{chr} = 2$ characterizes bipartite graphs, whereas $\mathrm{chr} = n$ characterizes the complete graph K_n. The independence number satisfies $1 \leq \mathrm{ind} \leq n - 1$. The lowest value $\mathrm{ind} = 1$ characterizes the complete graph K_n, while the highest value $\mathrm{ind} = n - 1$ characterizes the star graph on n vertices.

	K_n	C_n	Q_n	$K_{n,n}$	Petersen
chromatic	n	2 or 3	2	2	3
independence	1	$\lfloor n/2 \rfloor$	2^{n-1}	n	4

The chromatic number and the independence number are related by the following fact.

Proposition 2.1. If X is a graph on n vertices, then $\mathrm{chr}\, X \cdot \mathrm{ind}\, X \geq n$.

Proof. Consider a minimal colouring of X. The chromatic partition of the vertex set consists of $\mathrm{chr}\, X$ sets. Each monochromatic set of vertices is independent, so its size is at most $\mathrm{ind}\, X$. □

The obvious bound chr $\leq n$ can be improved as follows.

Proposition 2.2. Let X be a graph with maximal degree d. Then chr $X \leq d + 1$. If X is irregular, then chr $X \leq d$.

Proof. We argue by induction on the number of vertices. Consider the (possibly disconnected) graph X' obtained after deleting some vertex. It can be coloured by using $d + 1$ colours. The deleted vertex has at most d neighbours, so at least one more colour is available to complete the colouring.

The second part is argued similarly. Consider the graph X' obtained by deleting a vertex whose degree is less than d. We claim that X' can be coloured using d colours; by the choice of the deleted vertex, there is at least one colour available to complete the colouring. If X' is again irregular, then the claim holds by the induction hypothesis. If X' happens to be regular, then its degree is at most $d - 1$, so the claim holds thanks to the first part.   □

The first part of the previous proposition is sharp: complete graphs and odd cycles satisfy chr $= d + 1$. The second part suggests that some improvement is, however, possible. It turns out that the following holds.

Theorem 2.3 (Brooks). Let X be a graph with maximal degree d. If X is not a complete graph or an odd cycle, then chr $X \leq d$.

The original proof, but also the modern approaches, are somewhat involved. We have argued the easy case when the graph is not regular.

Notes. The chromatic number is the oldest graph invariant. Much of the early work in graph theory was motivated by a cartographic observation that we now call the four-colour theorem.

The reference for Theorem 2.3 is Brooks (*On colouring the nodes of a network*, Proc. Cambridge Philos. Soc. 1941; Zbl 0027.26403).

2.2 Diameter and girth

The *diameter* of a graph is the maximal distance between vertices. The *girth* of a graph is the minimal length of a cycle.

The diameter of a graph on n vertices satisfies $1 \leq \text{diam} \leq n - 1$. At the extremes, diam $= 1$ characterizes the complete graph K_n, and diam $= n - 1$ characterizes the path on n vertices. The girth satisfies $3 \leq \text{gir} \leq n$, unless we are dealing with a tree, in which case we put gir $= \infty$. The value gir $= n$ characterizes the cycle C_n.

	K_n	C_n	Q_n	$K_{n,n}$	Petersen
diameter	1	$\lfloor n/2 \rfloor$	n	2	2
girth	3	n	4	4	5

The diameter and the girth are related as follows.

Proposition 2.4. Let X be a graph which is not a tree. Then gir $X \leq 2 \cdot \text{diam } X + 1$. If gir X is even, then gir $X \leq 2 \cdot \text{diam } X$.

Proof. Consider a cycle of minimal length, and let δ' denote the intrinsic diameter of the cycle. Thus gir $X = 2\delta'$ or gir $X = 2\delta' + 1$, according to the parity. We have to show that diam $X \geq \delta'$.

Assume that, on the contrary, $\delta' > \text{diam } X$. Pick two vertices u and v on the cycle at distance δ', as measured along the cycle. On the other hand, u and v can be connected by a path no longer than diam X. So we have two paths from u to v whose lengths are equal to δ', respectively less than δ'. In particular, the two paths are distinct. It follows that there is a cycle whose length is less than $2\delta'$. As $2\delta' \leq \text{gir } X$, this is a contradiction. □

What about the extremal graphs with respect to the above bounds? That is, what can one say about graphs satisfying gir $X = 2 \cdot \text{diam } X + 1$, respectively gir $X = 2 \cdot \text{diam } X$? This turns out to be a good question in that it leads to interesting answers. Here are two highlights.

Theorem 2.5 (Damerell, Bannai–Ito). Let X be a regular graph with the property that gir $X = 2 \cdot \text{diam } X + 1$. If X is not an odd cycle, then the diameter of X is 1 or 2.

Theorem 2.6 (Feit–Higman, Singleton). Let X be a regular bipartite graph, satisfying gir $X = 2 \cdot \text{diam } X$. If X is not an even cycle, then the diameter of X is 2, 3, 4 or 6.

These two results basically say that, among regular graphs, the diameter and the girth can take only a few small values once we rule out the cycle graphs. The proofs are among the major accomplishments of spectral graph theory, but they are too involved to be included in this text.

Powerful as they are, the previous two theorems leave us with the issue of realizing the allowed values for the diameter. In Theorem 2.5, the case of diameter 1 is trivial, as it describes the family of complete graphs K_n. The case of diameter 2 is non-trivial, and we will return to it. We will find that there are very few possible graphs, one of which we already know: the Petersen graph. In Theorem 2.6, the case of diameter 2 is again trivial, and it covers the family of complete bipartite graphs $K_{n,n}$. It is known that there are infinite families of graphs realizing each of the remaining values 3, 4, and 6, for the diameter. The simplest such family, accounting for the case of diameter 3, will appear later on.

We now turn to another result, which gives bounds for diameter and the girth in terms of the fundamental parameters.

Theorem 2.7. Let X be a graph with maximal degree $d \geq 3$. Then we have

$$\text{diam } X > \frac{\log n}{\log(d-1)} - 2.$$

If X is also regular, then

$$\text{gir } X < 2\frac{\log n}{\log(d-1)} + 2.$$

Proof. Let u be a fixed vertex, and let us consider successive spheres around u. For each radius $r \geq 1$, we have $|S_r(u)| \leq (d-1)|S_{r-1}(u)|$, and so $|S_r(u)| \leq d(d-1)^{r-1}$. We can then bound the size of an r-ball as

$$|B_r(u)| \leq 1 + d + d(d-1) + \cdots + d(d-1)^{r-1} < d(d-1)^r.$$

Take $r = \text{diam } X$. Then the ball $B_r(u)$ is the entire vertex set, so $n < d(d-1)^r$. Therefore $\text{diam } X = r > \log_{d-1} n - \log_{d-1} d$. As $\log_{d-1} d < 2$, we get the claimed lower bound for the diameter.

We turn to the girth bound for regular graphs. Note, in passing, that the girth is well defined since a regular graph cannot be a tree. We now exploit the idea that, for a certain short range, balls around u achieve exponential growth in the radius. Namely, as long as $2r < \text{gir } X$, we have

$$|B_r(u)| = 1 + d + d(d-1) + \cdots + d(d-1)^{r-1} > (d-1)^r.$$

Therefore $n \geq |B_r(u)| > (d-1)^r$, in other words $r < \log_{d-1} n$. Taking r largest possible subject to $2r < \text{gir } X$, we have $\text{gir } X \leq 2r + 2$. The claimed upper bound follows.   □

The bounds of the previous theorem become particularly appealing when viewed in an asymptotic light. A *d-regular family* is an infinite sequence of d-regular graphs $\{X_k\}$ with $|X_k| \to \infty$. For a d-regular family with $d \geq 3$, Theorem 2.7 says that the diameter growth is at least logarithmic in the size, $\text{diam } X_k \gg \log|X_k|$, while the girth growth is at most logarithmic in the size, $\text{gir } X_k \ll \log|X_k|$. Here, we are using the following growth relation on sequences: $a_k \ll b_k$ if there is a constant C such that $a_k \leq Cb_k$ for all k.

At this point, it is natural, again, to ask about extremal families. A *d-regular family* $\{X_k\}$ is said to have *small diameter* if $\text{diam } X_k \asymp \log|X_k|$, respectively *large girth* if $\text{gir } X_k \asymp \log|X_k|$. The growth equivalence of sequences is defined as follows: $a_k \asymp b_k$ if and only if $a_k \ll b_k$ and $a_k \gg b_k$.

Example 2.8. We consider the rooted tree $\tilde{T}_{3,k}$, for $k \geq 3$, and we turn it into a 3-regular graph by adding edges between pendant vertices. Indeed, the pendant vertices have a natural partition into 4-tuples, induced by the vertices that lie two levels up. Let X_k be the graph obtained by turning every 4-tuple into a 4-cycle, in some way. It is easy to check that the 3-regular graph X_k has diameter $2k$, and $3 \cdot 2^k - 2$ vertices. Thus $\{X_k\}$ is a regular family of small diameter.

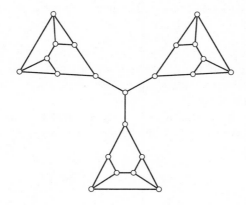

Figure 2.1. The graph X_3.

Notes. The references for Theorems 2.5 and 2.6 are Damerell (*On Moore graphs*, Proc. Cambridge Philos. Soc. 1973; Zbl 0262.05132) and Bannai and Ito (*On finite Moore graphs*, J. Fac. Sci. Univ. Tokyo Sect. 1A Math. 1973; Zbl 0275.05121); Feit and Higman (*The nonexistence of certain generalized polygons*, J. Algebra 1964; Zbl 0126.05303) and Singleton (*On minimal graphs of maximum even girth*, J. Combinatorial Theory 1966; Zbl 0168.44703).

Large-girth families exist, but constructions are more involved. A beautiful group-theoretic construction was given by Margulis (*Explicit constructions of graphs without short cycles and low density codes*, Combinatorica 1982; Zbl 0492.05044).

2.3 Isoperimetric number

For a non-empty vertex subset S in a graph X, the *boundary* ∂S is the set of edges connecting S to its complement S^c. Note that S and S^c have the same boundary.

The *isoperimetric constant* is given by

$$\text{iso } X = \min_S \frac{|\partial S|}{|S|},$$

where the minimum is taken over all vertex subsets S that contain no more than half the vertices. A set S, on which the minimum is attained, is said to be an *isoperimetric set*.

Finding the isoperimetric constant can be quite difficult, even on small or familiar graphs. Unlike all the previous graph invariants, which are integral, the isoperimetric constant is rational. It is therefore harder to limit possibilities in a trial-and-error approach. In concrete examples, it can be quite easy to give an upper bound, by means of a well-chosen vertex subset. However, proving a matching lower bound is usually much harder.

Example 2.9. Consider the cube graph Q_n. The binary strings starting in 0 define a subset S containing half the number of vertices of Q_n, and $|\partial S|/|S| = 1$ since every vertex in S has one boundary edge. Thus iso $Q_n \leq 1$. We claim that, in fact, iso $Q_n = 1$.

We think of Q_n as the product $K_2 \times \cdots \times K_2$. We wish to argue that iso$(X \times K_2) = 1$ whenever iso $X = 1$. As iso $K_2 = 1$, the bound iso$(X \times K_2) \leq 1$ is an instance of the general principle that

$$\text{iso}(X \times Y) \leq \min\{\text{iso } X, \text{iso } Y\}.$$

Indeed, let S be an isoperimetric subset in X. In $X \times Y$, the boundary of the subset $S \times Y$ is in bijection with $(\partial S) \times Y$. It follows that iso$(X \times Y) \leq$ iso X, and similarly for iso Y.

The trickier bit is to show that iso$(X \times K_2) \geq 1$. We visualize $X \times K_2$ as two 'horizontal' copies of X, $X_\bullet$ and $X_\circ$, with additional 'vertical' edges joining $v_\bullet$ to $v_\circ$ for each vertex v in X. A vertex subset S in $X \times K_2$ is of the form $A_\bullet \cup B_\circ$, where A and B are vertex subsets in X. The boundary of S in $X \times K_2$ has horizontal edges corresponding to the boundary of A, respectively B, in X, and vertical edges corresponding to the symmetric difference $A \triangle B$. Thus, $|\partial S| = |\partial A| + |\partial B| + |A \triangle B|$. We have to show that

$$|\partial A| + |\partial B| + |A \triangle B| \geq |A| + |B|$$

whenever $|A| + |B| \leq |X|$. If $|A|, |B| \leq |X|/2$, then we already have $|\partial A| \geq |A|$ and $|\partial B| \geq |B|$. If $|A| \geq |X|/2 \geq |B|$, then $|\partial B| \geq |B|$, $|\partial A| \geq |A^c| = |X| - |A| \geq |B|$ and $|A \triangle B| \geq |A| - |B|$. Adding up these inequalities completes the argument.

Exercise 2.10. Show that iso $K_n = \lceil n/2 \rceil$; iso $C_n = 2/\lfloor n/2 \rfloor$; iso $K_{n,n} = \lceil n^2/2 \rceil / n$; iso $= 1$ for the Petersen graph.

	K_n	C_n	Q_n	$K_{n,n}$	Petersen
isoperimetric	$\sim n/2$	$\sim 4/n$	1	$\sim n/2$	1

This table records our findings in asymptotic form: we write $a_n \sim b_n$ if $a_n/b_n \to 1$ as $n \to \infty$.

The isoperimetric constant clearly satisfies $0 < \text{iso} \le d$. Taking a subset S consisting of two adjacent vertices, the upper bound can be improved to $d - 1$. But a more careful argument, explained below, yields an upper bound of roughly $d/2$. Note, however, that the isoperimetric constant may exceed $d/2$. This is the case for K_n and $K_{n,n}$, for odd n.

Proposition 2.11. Let X be a graph on n vertices, with maximal degree d. Then

$$\text{iso } X \le \frac{d}{2} \cdot \frac{n+1}{n-1}.$$

Proof. For $1 \le s \le \lfloor n/2 \rfloor$, we let iso_s denote the minimum of $|\partial S|/|S|$ as S runs over vertex subsets of size s. An upper bound for iso_s is the average

$$\frac{1}{\#\{S : |S| = s\}} \sum_{|S|=s} \frac{|\partial S|}{|S|},$$

which we can actually compute. Any given edge is in the boundary of $2\binom{n-2}{s-1}$ subsets of size s, so the numerator is $\sum_{|S|=s} |\partial S| = 2|E|\binom{n-2}{s-1}$. The denominator is $s\binom{n}{s}$. Simplifying, we deduce that

$$\text{iso}_s \le \frac{2|E|(n-s)}{n(n-1)}.$$

As $2|E| \le dn$, we get

$$\text{iso } X = \min_{s \le \lfloor n/2 \rfloor} \text{iso}_s \le \min_{s \le \lfloor n/2 \rfloor} \frac{d(n-s)}{n-1} = \frac{d(n - \lfloor n/2 \rfloor)}{n-1},$$

which is actually slightly better than the claim. □

Exercise 2.12. Let β denote the isoperimetric constant. Show that balls around a vertex have a short-range exponential growth behaviour: $|B_r(u)| \ge (1 + \beta/d)^r$ as long as $|B_{r-1}(u)| \le n/2$. Conclude that

$$\text{diam } X \le \frac{2\log(n/2)}{\log(1 + \beta/d)} + 2.$$

Let us explain an important qualitative consequence of this exercise. A d-regular family $\{X_k\}$ is said to be an *expander* if the sequence of isoperimetric constants $\{\text{iso } X_k\}$ is bounded away from 0. This is a very interesting condition: roughly speaking, an expander family is an infinite sequence of sparse graphs which nevertheless maintain a sizable connectivity. Exercise 2.12 implies the following fact:

an expander family has small diameter. Note that the converse does not hold. The small-diameter family $\{X_k\}$ of Example 2.8 is not an expander. Indeed, if S is the set of vertices lying on one of the three main branches stemming from the root, then $|\partial S| = 1$ and $|S| = 2^k - 1$. Thus iso $X_k \to 0$ exponentially fast.

Notes. Among the five invariants under consideration, the isoperimetric constant is the youngest. To the best of our knowledge, it was introduced by Buser (*Cubic graphs and the first eigenvalue of a Riemann surface*, Math. Z. 1978; Zbl 0371.53032). Elsewhere, the isoperimetric constant is also called the Cheeger constant because it is the graph-theoretic analogue of an isoperimetric constant for manifolds, due to Cheeger (*A lower bound for the smallest eigenvalue of the Laplacian*, in 'Problems in analysis', Princeton University Press 1970; Zbl 0212.44903). Other sources call it conductance.

   Proposition 2.11 is due to Mohar (*Isoperimetric numbers of graphs*, J. Combin. Theory Ser. B 1989; Zbl 0719.05042).

3

Regular graphs

This chapter has two main themes. Firstly, we discuss constructions of regular graphs from groups. The most important notion here is that of a Cayley graph. Secondly, we introduce some types of regular graphs. Their common feature is that the number of neighbours shared by pairs of vertices is severely restricted.

3.1 Cayley graphs

Let G be a finite group. Let $S \subseteq G$ be a subset that does not contain the identity of G, and which is *symmetric* (i.e., closed under taking inverses) and *generating* (i.e., every element of G is a product of elements from S). The *Cayley graph* of G with respect to S has the elements of G as vertices, and an edge between every two vertices $g, h \in G$ satisfying $g^{-1}h \in S$. In other words, the neighbours of a vertex g are the vertices of the form gs, where $s \in S$.

The Cayley graph of G with respect to S an $|S|$-regular graph of size $|G|$. The assumptions on G and S reflect our standing convention that graphs should be finite, connected and simple.

Example 3.1. Let G be a group with n elements. The Cayley graph of G with respect to the set of non-identity elements of G is the complete graph K_n. The Cayley graph of $G \times \mathbb{Z}_2$ with respect to $G \times \{1\}$ is the complete bipartite graph $K_{n,n}$.

Example 3.2. The Cayley graph of $\mathbb{Z}_n$ with respect to $\{\pm 1\}$ is the cycle graph C_n.

Example 3.3. The Cayley graph of $(\mathbb{Z}_2)^n$ with respect to $\{e_i = (0, \ldots, 0, 1, 0, \ldots, 0) : i = 1, \ldots, n\}$ is the cube graph Q_n.

Example 3.4. The *halved cube graph* $\frac{1}{2}Q_n$ is defined as follows: its vertices are those binary strings of length n that have an even weight, and edges connect two such strings when they differ in precisely two slots. This is the Cayley graph of the subgroup $\{v \in (\mathbb{Z}_2)^n : \sum v_i = 0\}$ with respect to $\{e_i + e_j : 1 \leq i < j \leq n\}$.

Example 3.5 (The twins). Here we consider two Cayley graphs coming from the same group, $\mathbb{Z}_4 \times \mathbb{Z}_4$. The two symmetric generating sets are

$$S_1 = \{\pm(1, 0), \pm(0, 1), (2, 0), (0, 2)\},$$
$$S_2 = \{\pm(1, 0), \pm(0, 1), \pm(1, 1)\}.$$

The corresponding Cayley graphs are 6-regular graphs on 16 vertices. It is not hard to recognize the Cayley graph with respect to S_1 as the product $K_4 \times K_4$. The second Cayley graph, with respect to S_2, is known as the *Shrikhande graph*. Both are depicted in Figure 3.1. An amusing puzzle, left to the reader, is to check the pictures by finding an appropriate $\mathbb{Z}_4 \times \mathbb{Z}_4$ labelling. The more interesting one is, of course, the Shrikhande graph.

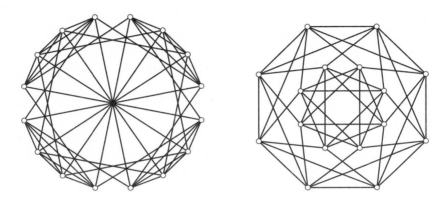

Figure 3.1. $K_4 \times K_4$ and the Shrikhande graph.

It seems quite appropriate to think of these two graphs as being twins. Not only are they Cayley graphs of the same group, but they also turn out to be indistinguishable by any of the five invariants under consideration! Both graphs have diameter 2 and girth 3. They also have the same chromatic number, 4. Indeed, we get a nice 4-colouring for both graphs by noting that the addition homomorphism $\mathbb{Z}_4 \times \mathbb{Z}_4 \to \mathbb{Z}_4$, given by $(a, b) \mapsto a + b$, is non-trivial on both sets of generators. On the other hand, three colours are not sufficient for $K_4 \times K_4$, as it contains K_4 as a subgraph; in the Shrikhande graph, it is the outer octagon that cannot be 3-coloured. Next, both graphs have independence number 4. Firstly, we know that ind ≥ 4 by using the inequality chr $\cdot$ ind ≥ 16. Secondly, we easily find independent sets of size 4 in each one of the two graphs. Finally, both graphs turn out to have isoperimetric constant 2. A conceptual explanation for this fact will be given later on, using spectral ideas.

Example 3.6. Let $n \geq 3$. The Cayley graph of $\mathbb{Z}_{3n-1}$ with respect to the symmetric generating set $S = \{1, 4, \ldots, 3n - 2\}$ is known as the *Andrásfai graph* A_n.

Exercise 3.7. Show that the Andrásfai graph A_n has diameter 2, girth 4, chromatic number 3, and independence number n.

Example 3.8. Let us view the five Platonic solids as graphs. The tetrahedron and the cube yield two familiar graphs, K_4 and Q_3. The next three are the octahedral graph (Figure 3.2), the icosahedral graph (Figure 3.3), and the dodecahedral graph (Figure 3.4).

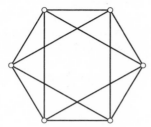 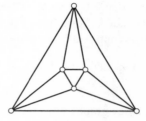

Figure 3.2. Two views of the octahedral graph.

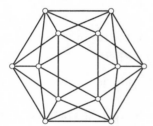 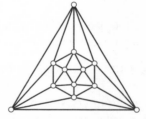

Figure 3.3. Two views of the icosahedral graph.

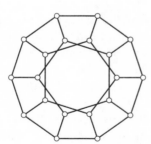 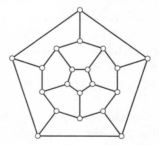

Figure 3.4. Two views of the dodecahedral graph.

The octahedral graph can be realized as the Cayley graph of $\mathbb{Z}_6$ with respect to $\{\pm 1, \pm 2\}$. Another realization is on the dihedral group with 6 elements. We think of this group as the semidirect product $\mathbb{Z}_3 \rtimes \{\pm 1\}$: the underlying set is $\mathbb{Z}_3 \times \{\pm 1\}$, with operation $(a, \epsilon)(b, \tau) = (a + \epsilon b, \epsilon \tau)$. The elements in $\mathbb{Z}_3 \times \{-1\}$ are involutions, and the remaining two non-trivial elements, $(\pm 1, 1)$, are inverse to each other. A symmetric subset S of size 4 must contain these two elements, and two more involutions picked from $\mathbb{Z}_3 \times \{-1\}$. The Cayley graph with respect to any one of the three possible choices for S is the octahedral graph. There is a good reason why this is the case: there is just one 4-regular graph on 6 vertices.

The icosahedral graph is a Cayley graph too. Namely, it is the Cayley graph of the alternating group Alt(4) with respect to the set $\{(123), (132), (234), (243), (12)(34)\}$.

Exercise 3.9. Let X be the Cayley graph of an abelian group. Show that diam $X \geq n^{1/d} - 1$.

Notes. Cayley graphs were introduced by Cayley in 1878.

3.2 Cayley graphs, continued

In this section, we carry on with our discussion of Cayley graphs. The following example highlights the usefulness of a Cayley graph perspective.

Example 3.10. As we know, a cube graph is bipartite. Is a cube graph a bipartite double?

We start from Q_{n+1}, and we look for an $(n + 1)$-regular graph on 2^n vertices. Adding one edge per vertex to Q_n would be such a graph. So let us consider the Cayley graph of $(\mathbb{Z}_2)^n$ with respect to $\{e_1, \ldots, e_n, a\}$, where the new generator $a \in (\mathbb{Z}_2)^n$ has weight greater than 1. This Cayley graph is referred to as the *decked cube graph* $DQ_n(a)$ in what follows.

A decked cube graph depends only on the weight of the new generator. Indeed, let a and a' have equal weight. Then we can actually set up a *Cayley graph isomorphism* between $DQ_n(a)$ and $DQ_n(a')$, that is, a group isomorphism between the underlying groups which maps one generating set onto the other. For there is a permutation of the basis $\{e_1, \ldots, e_n\}$ which, once extended to a group automorphism of $(\mathbb{Z}_2)^n$, maps a to a'.

A decked cube graph is bipartite if and only if the new generator has odd weight. To see this, consider the bipartition of Q_n according to weight parity. Then the new edges join vertices of different colour precisely when the weight of the new generator is odd.

So we focus on a decked cube graph $DQ_n(a)$ where $a \in (\mathbb{Z}_2)^n$ has even weight, and we claim that its bipartite double is Q_{n+1}. Note the following general fact: the bipartite double of the Cayley graph of a group G with respect to S is the Cayley graph of $G \times \mathbb{Z}_2$ with respect to $S \times \{1\}$. So the bipartite double of $DQ_n(a)$ is the Cayley graph of $(\mathbb{Z}_2)^{n+1}$ with respect to $\{(e_1, 1), \ldots, (e_n, 1), (a, 1)\}$. To show that the latter graph is Q_{n+1}, we use again a Cayley graph isomorphism. We adopt a linear algebra perspective, viewing $\mathbb{Z}_2$ as a field. Let A be the following $(n + 1)$-by-$(n + 1)$ matrix over $\mathbb{Z}_2$:

$$A = \begin{pmatrix} 1 & & & \\ & 1 & & \\ & & \ddots & \\ a_1 & \ldots & a_n & 1 \end{pmatrix}.$$

Then $v \mapsto Av$ defines a group homomorphism from $(\mathbb{Z}_2)^{n+1}$ to itself, mapping the standard basis $e'_1, \ldots, e'_{n+1}$ to $(e_1, 1), \ldots, (e_n, 1), (a, 1)$. It is, in fact, a group isomorphism, for the matrix A is invertible:

$$\det A = 1 + a_1 + \cdots + a_n = 1$$

since a has even weight.

Returning to our starting question, we infer that Q_{n+1} is a bipartite double as soon as there is an element of $(\mathbb{Z}_2)^n$ having even, but non-zero weight. This holds for $n \geq 2$, so all cube graphs starting from Q_3 are bipartite doubles. As for Q_2, it is not a bipartite double.

Cayley graphs appear to be highly symmetric. Let us formalize this idea. A graph is said to be *vertex-transitive* if any vertex can be taken to any other vertex by a graph automorphism.

Proposition 3.11. Cayley graphs are vertex-transitive.

Proof. Consider a Cayley graph of a group G. We look for a graph automorphism taking the identity vertex to an arbitrary vertex $g \in G$. Left multiplication by g, namely the mapping $h \mapsto gh$, does the job. $\qquad\square$

A vertex-transitive graph is, in particular, regular. Actually, a vertex-transitive graph has the same link graph at each vertex. This idea serves as an obstruction to vertex-transitivity. An illustration is provided by the regular graphs in Figure 1.6, whose link patterns reveal that they are not vertex-transitive. Also, we may speak of the link graph of a vertex-transitive graph, and we may read it off at any vertex. For instance, the link graph of $K_4 \times K_4$ is a disjoint union of two 3-cycles, and the link graph of the Shrikhande graph is a 6-cycle. So the twin graphs are, just as we suspected, not isomorphic.

Are there vertex-transitive graphs which are not Cayley graphs? The answer is positive, as one might guess, but providing examples is not an entirely trivial matter.

Example 3.12. The Petersen graph is vertex-transitive, but not a Cayley graph.

We first argue the vertex-transitivity. We think of the Petersen graph in its pentagram-within-a-pentagon drawing. Consider a labelling of the vertices as in the right-most panel of the triptych in Figure 3.5. Note that there is an obvious 5-fold rotational symmetry. So the vertices of the outer pentagon, 1 through 5, are in the same orbit of the automorphism group, and the same is true for the vertices of the inner pentagram, a through e. We need an automorphism that mixes up the two orbits. This is explained in the next two panels of Figure 3.5: switch b and 3, respectively e and 4, and then switch c and d. A mixing automorphism can be read off by comparing the first and the last panels.

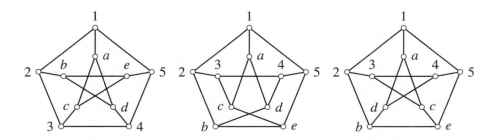

Figure 3.5.

The more elegant argument exploits the symbolic description of the Petersen graph. Recall, the Petersen graph records the relation of disjointness between 2-element subsets of a 5-element set Z. A permutation of Z maps 2-element subsets to 2-element subsets, and it does so in a disjointness-preserving fashion. So any permutation of Z defines an automorphism of the Petersen graph. Since any 2-element subset of Z can be taken to any other one by a permutation, we see that the Petersen graph is vertex-transitive.

We now argue that the Petersen graph is not a Cayley graph. Consider a Cayley graph having degree 3 and girth 5. There are two cases, according to whether the symmetric generating set S contains one or three involutions.

Let $S = \{r, s, t\}$, where $r^2 = s^2 = t^2 = 1$. The edges of a 5-cycle are labelled r, s, or t. Two consecutive edges have different labels, so one of the labels, say t, appears only once. Up to swapping r and s, we may assume that we have the labelling of Figure 3.6. Then $t = (rs)^2 = (sr)^2$. It follows that r commutes with t: $rt = r(sr)^2 = (rs)^2r = tr$. This means that there is a 4-cycle in the graph, a contradiction.

Let $S = \{r, a, a^{-1}\}$, where $r^2 = 1$. Again label the edges of a 5-cycle by the generators. There can be at most two occurrences of r. If there are two occurrences, then we get the relation $rar = a^{\pm 2}$ (Figure 3.7). But then $a = ra^{\pm 2}r = (rar)^{\pm 2} = a^4$, meaning that $a^3 = 1$. This yields a 3-cycle in the graph, hence a contradiction. If there is only one occurrence of r, then we get $r = a^4$ (Figure 3.8). The commutation relation $ar = ra$ yields a 4-cycle in the graph, a contradiction. The remaining case is

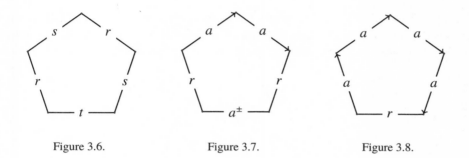

Figure 3.6.   Figure 3.7.   Figure 3.8.

no occurrence of r in the chosen 5-cycle. But the Petersen graph contains two 5-cycles sharing an edge, and it cannot be that both 5-cycles have no occurrences of r.

Example 3.13. The dodecahedral graph is vertex-transitive, but not a Cayley graph.

Indeed, the same argument as for the Petersen graph shows that the dodecahedral graph fails to be a Cayley graph. On the other hand, we observe that the five Platonic graphs are vertex-transitive. For, thinking of the five Platonic solids, we see that reflections take any face to any other face, and that, within each face, we can get from any vertex to any other vertex through rotations. But vertex-transitivity is only interesting for the dodecahedral graph — the other four Platonic graphs are, in fact, Cayley graphs.

We now turn to a bipartite variation on the notion of a Cayley graph. Let G be a finite group, and let $S \subseteq G$ be a subset which need not be symmetric, or which might contain the identity. A Cayley graph of G with respect to S can still be defined, but it will have directed edges or loops. Subsequently passing to a simple undirected graph, by forgetting directions and erasing loops, does not reflect the choice of S. An appropriate undirected substitute for the Cayley graph of G with respect to S can be constructed as follows. This illustrates the general procedure of turning a graph with directed edges and loops into a simple graph, by a bipartite construction.

The *bi-Cayley graph* of G with respect to S is the bipartite graph on two copies of G, $G_\bullet$ and $G_\circ$, in which $g_\bullet$ is adjacent to $h_\circ$ whenever $g^{-1}h \in S$. This is a regular graph, of degree $|S|$. It is connected if and only if the symmetric subset $S \cdot S^{-1} = \{st^{-1} : s, t \in S\}$ generates G. This is stronger than requiring S to generate G, though equivalent if S happens to contain the identity. Connectivity of a bi-Cayley graph may be cumbersome as a direct algebraic verification but in many cases this task is facilitated by alternate descriptions of the graph. The bi-Cayley graph of G with respect to S can also be defined as the bipartite graph on two copies of G, in which $g_\bullet$ is adjacent to $h_\circ$ whenever $gh \in S$. This adjacency law is more symmetric, and tends to appear more often in practice. The correspondence $g_\bullet \leftrightarrow (g^{-1})_\bullet$, $h_\circ \leftrightarrow h_\circ$ shows the equivalence of the two descriptions.

Example 3.14. The bi-Cayley graph of $\mathbb{Z}_7$ with respect to $S = \{1, 2, 4\}$ is the *Heawood graph*; see Figure 3.9. An interesting observation is that, when computing the difference set $S - S$, every non-zero element of $\mathbb{Z}_7$ appears exactly once.

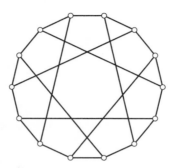

Figure 3.9. The Heawood graph.

There are two useful observations regarding the bi-Cayley construction. Firstly, if S is such that the Cayley graph of G with respect to S already makes sense, then its bipartite double is the bi-Cayley graph of G with respect to S. We interpret this as saying that the bi-Cayley graph construction is essentially a generalization of the Cayley graph construction.

Secondly, the bi-Cayley graph of G with respect to S is a Cayley graph in many cases of interest. Namely, assume G is an abelian group, and consider the semidirect product $G \rtimes \{\pm 1\}$ given by inversion. This means that we endow the set $G \times \{\pm 1\}$ with the non-abelian operation $(g, \epsilon)(h, \tau) = (gh^\epsilon, \epsilon\tau)$ for $g, h \in G$ and $\epsilon, \tau \in \{\pm 1\}$. If G happens to be a cyclic group, then $G \rtimes \{\pm 1\}$ is a dihedral group. This familiar instance prompts us to deem $G \rtimes \{\pm 1\}$ a *generalized dihedral group*. The advantage of the semidirect product over the direct product $G \times \{\pm 1\}$ is that now $S \times \{-1\}$ is symmetric in $G \rtimes \{\pm 1\}$, for it consists of involutions. The Cayley graph of $G \rtimes \{\pm 1\}$ with respect to $S \times \{-1\}$ is a bipartite graph on $G \times \{+1\}$ and $G \times \{-1\}$, with $(g, +1)$ connected to $(h, -1)$ whenever $g^{-1}h \in S$. This is precisely the bi-Cayley graph of G with respect to S.

3.3 Strongly regular graphs

A regular graph is said to be *strongly regular* if there are two non-negative integers a and c such that any two adjacent vertices have a common neighbours, and any two distinct non-adjacent vertices have c common neighbours.

Example 3.15. The Petersen graph is strongly regular, with $a = 0$ and $c = 1$.

Example 3.16. The cycle C_5 is strongly regular, with $a = 0$ and $c = 1$. The only other cycle which is strongly regular is C_4, which has $a = 0$ and $c = 2$.

Example 3.17. The complete bipartite graph $K_{n,n}$ is strongly regular, with $a = 0$ and $c = n$. No other bipartite graph is strongly regular.

Example 3.18. The rook's graph $K_n \times K_n$ is strongly regular, with $a = n - 2$ and $c = 2$. No other non-trivial product is strongly regular.

Example 3.19. The twin graphs, $K_4 \times K_4$ and the Shrikhande graph, are strongly regular with $a = c = 2$.

The complete graph K_n has $a = n - 2$ but undefined c. Treating it as a strongly regular graph is a matter of convention, and ours is to exclude it.

The parameters (n, d, a, c) of a strongly regular graph are constrained by a number of relations. The simplest one is the following:

Proposition 3.20. The parameters (n, d, a, c) of a strongly regular graph satisfy

$$d(d - a - 1) = (n - d - 1)c.$$

Proof. Fix a base vertex; its link graph has d vertices, and there are $n - d - 1$ farther vertices. The desired relation comes from counting in two ways the edges between link vertices and farther vertices.

Each link vertex has a common neighbours with the base vertex. In other words, the link graph is a-regular. So each link vertex is adjacent to $d - a - 1$ farther vertices.

Each farther vertex has c common neighbours with the base vertex. That is, each farther vertex is adjacent to c link vertices. $\square$

As we have seen, the link graph of any vertex is an a-regular graph on d vertices. It cannot be complete on d vertices — if it were, the whole graph would be complete on $d + 1$ vertices. So $a < d - 1$, and $c > 0$. The latter fact means the following.

Proposition 3.21. A strongly regular graph has diameter 2.

There are non-isomorphic strongly regular graphs with the same parameters (n, d, a, c). For example, the twin graphs have parameters $(16, 6, 2, 2)$. The following construction provides many more examples of this kind.

Theorem 3.22. Fix a positive integer n. Let G be a finite group with n elements, and let X_G be the Cayley graph of $G \times G$ with respect to the symmetric generating subset $\{(s, 1), (1, s), (s, s) : s \in G, s \neq 1\}$. Then

(i) X_G is strongly regular with parameters $(n^2, 3n - 3, n, 6)$;

(ii) the number of elements of order 2 in G is a graph invariant of X_G.

Proof. Part (i) is straightforward counting. Pick two distinct vertices in X_G, one of which may be assumed to be the identity $(1, 1)$. If the other vertex, say (x, y), is adjacent to $(1, 1)$, then (x, y) is of the form (s, s), or $(s, 1)$, or $(1, s)$ with $s \neq 1$. We count n common neighbours in each case: $(s, 1)$, $(1, s)$, and (t, t) with $t \neq 1, s$; (s, s), $(1, s^{-1})$, and $(t, 1)$ with $t \neq 1, s$; (s, s), $(s^{-1}, 1)$, and $(1, t)$ with $t \neq 1, s$. Now take a vertex (x, y) not adjacent to $(1, 1)$, meaning that $x \neq 1$, $y \neq 1$, and $x \neq y$. Then (x, y) has six common neighbours with $(1, 1)$, namely (x, x) and (y, y), $(x, 1)$ and $(xy^{-1}, 1)$, $(1, y)$ and $(1, yx^{-1})$.

(ii) Consider the link graph of X_G. It has $3n - 3$ vertices, and it is n-regular. The vertices of the link at $(1, 1)$ are naturally partitioned into three 'islands': $S_1 = \{(s, 1) : s \neq 1\}$, $S_2 = \{(1, s) : s \neq 1\}$, and $S_3 = \{(s, s) : s \neq 1\}$. Each S_i is a complete subgraph on $n - 1$ vertices. A vertex has $n - 2$ incident edges within its own island, and two more 'bridge' edges connecting it to the remaining two islands. It follows that 3-cycles in the link graph are either contained in an island, or they consist of three vertices from each of the islands, connected by bridge edges. The number of 3-cycles contained in an island is a function of n. The number of 3-cycles of bridge type equals the number of elements of order 2 in G. Indeed, the paths of length 3 starting and ending in S_2, say along bridge edges, have the form $(s, 1) \sim (s, s) \sim (1, s) \sim (s^{-1}, 1)$. This is a 3-cycle precisely when s has order 2. In conclusion, the number of elements of order 2 in G is a graph invariant of the link graph of X_G, hence of X_G itself, when the order of G is fixed. $\qquad\square$

Corollary 3.23. For every positive integer N, there exist N strongly regular graphs that are pairwise non-isomorphic, but have the same parameters.

Proof. For $k = 1, \ldots, N$, consider the abelian group $G(k) = (\mathbb{Z}_2)^{k-1} \times \mathbb{Z}_{2^{N-k}}$. Then $G(k)$ has size 2^{N-1}, and $2^k - 1$ elements of order 2. The previous theorem implies that the graphs $X_{G(k)}$, $k = 1, \ldots, N$ are strongly regular with the same parameters, but they are mutually non-isomorphic. $\qquad\square$

Exercise 3.24. Consider the abelian group $(\mathbb{Z}_2)^n \times (\mathbb{Z}_2)^n$, where $n \geq 2$. Put $m = 2^n$. Show that the Cayley graphs with respect to the subsets

$$S = \left\{(x, y) \in (\mathbb{Z}_2)^n \times (\mathbb{Z}_2)^n : x_1 y_1 + \cdots + x_n y_n = 1\right\},$$
$$S' = \{(x, y) \in (\mathbb{Z}_2)^n \times (\mathbb{Z}_2)^n : x_1 + y_1 + x_1 y_1 + \cdots + x_n y_n = 1\}$$

are strongly regular, with parameters $\left(m^2, \frac{1}{2}(m^2 - m), \frac{1}{4}(m^2 - 2m), \frac{1}{4}(m^2 - 2m)\right)$ in the case of S, respectively $\left(m^2, \frac{1}{2}(m^2 + m), \frac{1}{4}(m^2 + 2m), \frac{1}{4}(m^2 + 2m)\right)$ in the case of S'.

Notes. Strongly regular graphs were introduced by Bose (*Strongly regular graphs, partial geometries and partially balanced designs*, Pacific Jour. Math. 1963;

Zbl 0118.33903). The Shrikhande graph was originally defined by Shrikhande (*The uniqueness of the L_2 association scheme*, Ann. Math. Stat. 1959; Zbl 0086.34802) in a combinatorial way that made strong regularity immediate.

3.4 Design graphs

Next, we consider bipartite analogues of strongly regular graphs.

A *design graph* is a regular bipartite graph with the property that any two distinct vertices of the same colour have the same number of common neighbours. The complete bipartite graph $K_{n,n}$ fits the definition, but we exclude it by convention.

For a design graph, we let m denote the half-size, d the degree, and c the number of neighbours shared by any monochromatic pair of vertices. Note that the parameter c is, in fact, determined by the following relation:

$$c(m - 1) = d(d - 1).$$

This is obtained by counting in two ways the paths of length 2 joining a fixed vertex with the remaining $m - 1$ vertices of the same colour.

As an immediate consequence of the definition, we have following fact.

Proposition 3.25. A design graph has diameter 3, and girth 4 or 6 according to whether $c > 1$ or $c = 1$. Conversely, a regular bipartite graph of diameter 3 and girth 6 is a design graph with parameter $c = 1$.

Design graphs with parameter $c = 1$ are particularly interesting. The previous proposition highlights them as being extremal for the girth among regular bipartite graphs of diameter 3. The next exercise is concerned with another extremal property.

Exercise 3.26. Show that d-regular design graphs of girth 6 are precisely the ones that minimize the number of vertices among all d-regular graphs of girth 6.

It seems appropriate to refer to design graphs with parameter $c = 1$ as *extremal design graphs*. There are some examples of extremal design graphs among the graphs that we already know. One is the cycle C_6. The other, more interesting one is the Heawood graph. In the next chapter, we will construct more design graphs, some of them extremal, by using finite fields.

A *partial design graph* is a regular bipartite graph with the property that there are only two possible values for the number of neighbours shared by any two distinct vertices of the same colour.

The parameters of a partial design graph are denoted m and d, respectively c_1 and c_2. Note that $c_1 \neq c_2$, and that the roles of c_1 and c_2 are interchangeable.

Example 3.27. The bipartite double of a (non-bipartite) strongly regular graph is a design graph or a partial design graph.

Example 3.28. The cube graph Q_n is a partial design graph. Indeed, consider the bipartition given by weight parity. Fix two distinct strings with the same weight parity. If they differ in two slots, then they have two common neighbours; otherwise, they have no common neighbour. Thus, Q_n has parameters $c_1 = 0$, $c_2 = 2$.

Example 3.29. Consider the complete graph K_6. It has 15 edges. A *matching* is a choice of three edges with distinct endpoints, that is, a partition of the six vertices into two-element subsets. There are 15 matchings as well. Define a bipartite graph by using the edges and the matchings as vertices, and connecting matchings to the edges they contain. This is the *Tutte–Coxeter graph*, drawn in Figure 3.10.

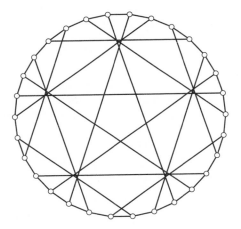

Figure 3.10. The Tutte–Coxeter graph.

The Tutte–Coxeter graph is a partial design graph. Its half-size is $m = 15$. The degree is $d = 3$. Indeed, a matching is adjacent to three edges, and an edge is adjacent to three matchings. The joint parameters are $c_1 = 0$, $c_2 = 1$. Two distinct edges are adjacent to a unique matching if they have disjoint endpoints, and to no matching otherwise. Two distinct matchings have at most one edge in common.

A further property of the Tutte–Coxeter graph is that it has diameter 4 and girth 8. The verification is left to the reader.

4

Finite fields

In this chapter, and in the next one, the focus is on finite fields. Among other things, we construct some interesting families of graphs, and we acquire some of the tools that later on will prove useful for studying these graphs.

4.1 Notions

Let us start by recalling some fundamental facts about finite fields.

A finite field has $q = p^d$ elements for some prime p, the characteristic of the field, and some positive integer d, the dimension of the field over its prime subfield.

For each prime power q there exists a field with q elements, which is furthermore unique up to isomorphism. We think of $\mathbb{Z}_p = \mathbb{Z}/p\mathbb{Z}$ as 'the' field with p elements. In general, 'the' field with $q = p^d$ elements can be realized as a quotient $\mathbb{Z}_p[X]/(f(X))$, where $f(X) \in \mathbb{Z}_p[X]$ is an irreducible polynomial of degree d. Such a polynomial f exists for each given d; however, no general recipe is known for producing one.

The multiplicative group of a finite field is cyclic. This is, again, a non-constructive existence: given a field, there is no known recipe for producing a multiplicative generator.

We now turn to extensions of finite fields. The following result plays a key role in this respect.

Theorem 4.1. Let $\mathbb{K}$ be a field with q^n elements. Then the map $\phi : \mathbb{K} \to \mathbb{K}$, given by $\phi(a) = a^q$, has the following properties:

   (i) ϕ is an automorphism of $\mathbb{K}$ of order n;
   (ii) $\mathbb{F} = \{a \in \mathbb{K} : \phi(a) = a\}$ is a field with q elements, and ϕ is an $\mathbb{F}$-linear isomorphism when $\mathbb{K}$ is viewed as a linear space over $\mathbb{F}$.

Proof. (i) Clearly, ϕ is injective, multiplicative, and $\phi(1) = 1$. To see that ϕ is additive, we iterate the basic identity $(a + b)^p = a^p + b^p$, where p is the characteristic of $\mathbb{K}$, up to $(a + b)^q = a^q + b^q$. Thus ϕ is an automorphism of $\mathbb{K}$. Each $a \in \mathbb{K}^*$ satisfies the relation $a^{q^n - 1} = 1$, so $a^{q^n} = a$ for all $a \in \mathbb{K}$. Thus ϕ^n is the identity map on $\mathbb{K}$. Assuming that ϕ^t is the identity map on $\mathbb{K}$ for some $0 < t < n$, we would get that $X^{q^t} = X$ has q^n solutions in $\mathbb{K}$, a contradiction.

(ii) $\mathbb{F}$ is a subfield since ϕ is an automorphism. As $\mathbb{K}^*$ is cyclic of order $q^n - 1$, and $q - 1$ divides $q^n - 1$, there are precisely $q - 1$ elements $a \in \mathbb{K}^*$ satisfying $a^{q-1} = 1$. Therefore $\mathbb{F}$ has q elements. Finally, note that $\phi(ab) = \phi(a)\phi(b) = a\phi(b)$ whenever $a \in \mathbb{F}$ and $b \in \mathbb{K}$.   □

Turning the above theorem on its head, we can start with a field $\mathbb{F}$ with q elements, and then consider a field $\mathbb{K}$ with q^n elements as an overfield of $\mathbb{F}$. Then $\mathbb{K}$ is an n-dimensional linear space over $\mathbb{F}$, and we say that $\mathbb{K}$ is an *extension* of $\mathbb{F}$ of *degree n*. The map ϕ is called the *Frobenius automorphism* of $\mathbb{K}$ over $\mathbb{F}$.

Exercise 4.2. Let $\mathbb{F}$ be a field with q elements. Show that the maximal order of an element in the general linear group $\mathrm{GL}_n(\mathbb{F})$ is $q^n - 1$.

Let $\mathbb{F}$ be a field with q elements, and let $\mathbb{K}$ be an extension of $\mathbb{F}$ of degree n. The *trace* and the *norm* of an element $a \in \mathbb{K}$ are defined as

$$\mathrm{Tr}(a) = \sum_{k=0}^{n-1} \phi^k(a) = a + a^q + \cdots + a^{q^{n-1}},$$

$$\mathrm{Nm}(a) = \prod_{k=0}^{n-1} \phi^k(a) = a \cdot a^q \cdot \ldots \cdot a^{q^{n-1}}.$$

One might think of the trace and the norm as the additive, respectively the multiplicative, content of a Frobenius orbit. The importance of the trace and the norm stems from the following properties.

Theorem 4.3. The trace is additive, in fact $\mathbb{F}$-linear, while the norm is multiplicative. The trace and the norm map $\mathbb{K}$ onto $\mathbb{F}$.

Proof. The first statement is obvious, so let us turn to the second statement. The trace and the norm are Frobenius invariant, $\phi(\mathrm{Tr}(a)) = \mathrm{Tr}(a)$ and $\phi(\mathrm{Nm}(a)) = \mathrm{Nm}(a)$, so they are $\mathbb{F}$-valued. Consider $\mathrm{Tr} : \mathbb{K} \to \mathbb{F}$ as an additive homomorphism. The size of its kernel is at most q^{n-1}, so the size of its image is at least $q^n/q^{n-1} = q$. Therefore the trace map is onto. Similarly, consider $\mathrm{Nm} : \mathbb{K}^* \to \mathbb{F}^*$ as a multiplicative homomorphism. Its kernel has size at most $(q^n - 1)/(q - 1)$, so the size of its image is at least $q - 1$. A fortiori, the norm map is onto.   □

Exercise 4.4. Show that the kernels of the trace and the norm maps can be described as

$$\{a \in \mathbb{K} : \mathrm{Tr}(a) = 0\} = \{b^q - b : b \in \mathbb{K}\},$$
$$\{a \in \mathbb{K} : \mathrm{Nm}(a) = 1\} = \{b^q/b : b \in \mathbb{K}^*\}.$$

Example 4.5. Let us discuss in some detail the simple case of degree 2, or *quadratic*, extensions. We give a fairly concrete picture for such an extension, its Frobenius automorphism, and the associated trace and norm maps. We do this in odd characteristic, and we invite the reader to provide a similar discussion in even characteristic.

Let $\mathbb{F}$ be a finite field of odd characteristic. The squaring map $\mathbb{F} \to \mathbb{F}$, given by $x \mapsto x^2$, is not injective hence not surjective either. Let $d \in \mathbb{F}$ be a non-square, that is, an element not in the range of the squaring map. Then the quadratic polynomial $X^2 - d \in \mathbb{F}[X]$ is irreducible, and

$$\mathbb{K} = \mathbb{F}[X]/(X^2 - d) = \{x + y\sqrt{d} : x, y \in \mathbb{F}\}$$

is a quadratic extension of $\mathbb{F}$. We use $\sqrt{d}$ to denote the class of X in $\mathbb{F}[X]/(X^2 - d)$.

The Frobenius automorphism of $\mathbb{K}$ over $\mathbb{F}$ is determined by what it does on $\sqrt{d}$. As $\phi(\sqrt{d})^2 = \phi(d) = d = (\sqrt{d})^2$, we infer that $\phi(\sqrt{d}) = \pm\sqrt{d}$. Now $\sqrt{d}$ cannot be fixed by ϕ, since $\sqrt{d} \notin \mathbb{F}$, so $\phi(\sqrt{d}) = -\sqrt{d}$. Therefore ϕ is the 'conjugation'

$$\phi(x + y\sqrt{d}) = x - y\sqrt{d}.$$

The trace and the norm are then given as

$$\mathrm{Tr}(x + y\sqrt{d}) = (x + y\sqrt{d}) + (x - y\sqrt{d}) = 2x,$$
$$\mathrm{Nm}(x + y\sqrt{d}) = (x + y\sqrt{d})(x - y\sqrt{d}) = x^2 - dy^2.$$

4.2 Projective combinatorics

Let $\mathbb{F}$ be a field with q elements, and consider a linear space V of dimension n over $\mathbb{F}$. We think of V as an ambient space, and we investigate the combinatorics of its subspaces. A k-dimensional subspace of V is called a k-space in what follows.

The number of k-spaces is denoted by

$$\binom{n}{k}_q.$$

These numbers are called *q-binomial coefficients*. The notation and the name suggest a certain analogy with the usual binomial coefficients. In fact, a fruitful and intriguing heuristic principle relates subspace combinatorics over finite fields with subset combinatorics. This principle says that subset combinatorics is the formal degeneration of subspace combinatorics, obtained by evaluating at $q = 1$.

Proposition 4.6. The number of k-spaces is given by the following explicit formula:

$$\binom{n}{k}_q = \frac{(q^n - 1) \cdots (q^{n-k+1} - 1)}{(q^k - 1) \cdots (q - 1)}. \tag{4.1}$$

Proof. There are $(q^n - 1) \cdots (q^n - q^{k-1})$ ordered ways of choosing k linearly independent vectors. However, some of these choices span one and the same k-space. As the
case $n = k$ of the previous count, we know that a k-space has $(q^k - 1) \cdots (q^k - q^{k-1})$
ordered bases. Dividing out, and suitably cancelling powers of q, we obtain the
desired formula.   □

Exercise 4.7. How many direct summands does a k-space have?

The first instance of the heuristic principle announced above is that the q-binomial
coefficients turn into the usual binomial coefficients when $q = 1$. We can already
make sense of this as a limit, by formally letting $q \to 1$ in the formula (4.1).

It is then to be expected that familiar relations between the usual binomial coefficients have q-analogues. We record the two simplest ones. They are easily checked
using the explicit formula (4.1).

Proposition 4.8. The q-binomial coefficients are symmetric,

$$\binom{n}{k}_q = \binom{n}{n-k}_q, \tag{4.2}$$

and they satisfy the Pascal recurrence

$$\binom{n}{k}_q = \binom{n-1}{k-1}_q + q^k \binom{n-1}{k}_q = q^{n-k} \binom{n-1}{k-1}_q + \binom{n-1}{k}_q. \tag{4.3}$$

An interesting consequence of the recurrence (4.3), which is not immediately clear
from (4.1), is the following: the q-binomial coefficient $\binom{n}{k}_q$ is a monic polynomial
of degree $k(n - k)$, with positive integral coefficients. So, these coefficients count
something! Their combinatorial interpretation should, in particular, account for the
idea that the q-binomial coefficients turn into the usual binomial coefficients when
$q = 1$. Note that a direct evaluation now makes sense, whereas previously the rational
form (4.1) required a limit.

Recall that there is a correspondence between the k-spaces of $\mathbb{F}^n$, and $k \times n$
matrices in reduced echelon form. Such a matrix has a 1 as the first non-zero entry
in each row, and each subsequent row has the leading 1 further to the right, with the
entries above it all zero; the following matrix is an example:

$$\begin{pmatrix} 0 & 1 & 0 & * & * & 0 & * \\ & & 1 & * & * & 0 & * \\ & & & & & 1 & * \end{pmatrix}.$$

The underlying relation is that a k-space is the row space of the corresponding $k \times n$
matrix.

To each k-space we can then associate a k-set, by recording the columns of the leading 1s in the corresponding $k \times n$ matrix. The resulting map, from k-spaces to k-sets, is clearly onto. The number of k-spaces mapping to a k-set $S = \{i_1 < i_2 < \cdots < i_k\}$ is $q^{\sigma(S)}$, where $\sigma(S)$ is the reduced sum

$$\sigma(S) = i_1 + i_2 + \cdots + i_k - \frac{k(k+1)}{2}.$$

The reduced sum σ lands in $\{0, \ldots, k(n-k)\}$, and it achieves every value therein. We conclude that

$$\binom{n}{k}_q = \sum_{S \ k\text{-set}} q^{\sigma(S)} = \sum_{s=0}^{k(n-k)} N_s q^s, \tag{4.4}$$

where N_s is the number of k-sets whose reduced sum equals s.

The combinatorics of subspaces can be given an additional twist, of geometrical flavour, with the help of a scalar product. A *scalar product* on V is a bilinear form $\langle \cdot, \cdot \rangle : V \times V \rightarrow \mathbb{F}$ which is symmetric, $\langle v, w \rangle = \langle w, v \rangle$ for all $v, w \in V$, and non-degenerate, meaning that $\langle v, w \rangle = 0$ for all $w \in V$ implies $v = 0$. The obvious example is the standard scalar product on $\mathbb{F}^n$, given by $\langle x, y \rangle = x_1 y_1 + \cdots + x_n y_n$. For a more interesting example, let $\mathbb{K}$ be a degree-n extension of $\mathbb{F}$. Then $\mathbb{K}$ can be endowed with the tracial scalar product $\langle a, b \rangle_\tau = \text{Tr}(ab)$. In general, any ambient space V can be equipped with a scalar product.

A scalar product brings in the notion of orthogonality. In particular, for a subspace W of V we can define

$$W^\perp = \{v \in V : \langle v, w \rangle = 0 \text{ for all } w \in W\},$$

which is again a subspace of V. For the standard scalar product over the real numbers, we would call $W^\perp$ the orthogonal complement of W. In general, however, there is a catch: $W^\perp$ may fail to be a direct summand of W, because a non-zero vector can be orthogonal to itself. This is particularly visible in the case of the standard scalar product on $\mathbb{F}^n$, the point being that the equation $X_1^2 + \cdots + X_n^2 = 0$ admits non-zero solutions in $\mathbb{F}$.

Nevertheless, the following holds.

Proposition 4.9. Let V be endowed with a scalar product. Then the map $W \mapsto W^\perp$ is an involutive correspondence between the k-spaces and the $(n-k)$-spaces of V.

Proof. The main claim is that $W^\perp$ is an $(n-k)$-space, whenever W is a k-space. For then $W^{\perp\perp}$ is, again, a k-space. Consequently, the inclusion $W \subseteq W^{\perp\perp}$ has to be an equality, and this precisely means that $W \mapsto W^\perp$ is an involution.

In order to prove the above dimensional claim, we first establish the following fact, interesting on its own: each basis $v_1, \ldots, v_n$ of V has a unique 'dual basis'

$v_1^*, \ldots, v_n^*$ with the property that $\langle v_i^*, v_j \rangle = \delta_{ij}$ for all $1 \le i, j \le n$. Indeed, consider the map $\psi : V \to \mathbb{F}^n$ given by $\psi(v) = (\langle v, v_1 \rangle, \ldots, \langle v, v_n \rangle)$. Then ψ is linear and injective, hence an isomorphism for dimension reasons. Let $v_1^*, \ldots, v_n^* \in V$ be the pre-images of the standard vectors $e_1, \ldots, e_n \in \mathbb{F}^n$. Then $\langle v_i^*, v_j \rangle$ is the jth component of $\psi(v_i^*) = e_i$, that is, δ_{ij}. The uniqueness part is easy, and it is left to the reader.

Now let $w_1, \ldots, w_k$ be a basis of W. Complete it to a basis of V, by adding vectors $v_1, \ldots, v_{n-k}$, and consider the dual basis $w_1^*, \ldots, w_k^*, v_1^*, \ldots, v_{n-k}^*$. Then $v_1^*, \ldots, v_{n-k}^*$ are in $W^\perp$, since they are orthogonal to $w_1, \ldots, w_k$. We check that $v_1^*, \ldots, v_{n-k}^*$ span, in fact, $W^\perp$; it will then follow that $\dim W^\perp = n - k$. Let $u \in W^\perp$. Then u is a linear combination of w_i^*'s and v_j^*'s. But the coefficient of each w_i^* is $\langle u, w_i \rangle = 0$, so u is in fact a linear combination of v_j^*'s only.   □

This proposition offers, in particular, a conceptual explanation for the symmetry of the q-binomial coefficients (4.2).

We end with the following fact, which we will soon find to be rather useful.

Proposition 4.10. The number of m-spaces containing a given k-space is $\binom{n-k}{m-k}_q$.

Proof. This can be seen in two ways. One is to pass to the quotient space of the ambient space V by the given k-space, and then count the $(m-k)$-spaces in an ambient $(n-k)$-dimensional space. The other is to use the above correspondence $W \mapsto W^\perp$, after having endowed V with a scalar product. The involution $W \mapsto W^\perp$ is order reversing with respect to inclusion, that is, $W_1 \subseteq W_2$ if and only if $W_2^\perp \subseteq W_1^\perp$. So the number of m-spaces containing a given k-space equals the number of $(n-m)$-spaces contained in a given $(n-k)$-space. The latter count yields $\binom{n-k}{n-m}_q$ which, by symmetry, equals $\binom{n-k}{m-k}_q$.   □

Notes. Our explanation for formula (4.4) draws from Knuth (*Subspaces, subsets, and partitions*, J. Combinatorial Theory Ser. A 1971; Zbl 0221.05024). A closely related combinatorial interpretation, in terms of lattice paths, was given earlier by Pólya (*On the number of certain lattice polygons*, J. Combinatorial Theory 1969). One could argue, however, that formula (4.4) should be ascribed to Sylvester.

4.3 Incidence graphs

Let V be an ambient linear space of dimension $n \ge 3$ over a finite field $\mathbb{F}$ with q elements. The *incidence graph* $I_n(q)$ is the bipartite graph whose vertices are the 1-spaces respectively the $(n-1)$-spaces, and whose edges connect 1-spaces to $(n-1)$-spaces containing them. Note that the construction depends only on the dimension of V, and not on V itself; hence the notation.

Theorem 4.11. The incidence graph $I_n(q)$ is a design graph, with parameters

$$m = \binom{n}{1}_q = \frac{q^n - 1}{q - 1}, \qquad d = \binom{n-1}{1}_q = \frac{q^{n-1} - 1}{q - 1}, \qquad c = \binom{n-2}{1}_q = \frac{q^{n-2} - 1}{q - 1}.$$

Proof. By definition, the incidence graph $I_n(q)$ is bipartite. The half-size m and the degree d for each vertex are easily counted. To check the design property, we use the dimensional formula

$$\dim(W + W') + \dim(W \cap W') = \dim W + \dim W',$$

where W and W' are subspaces of V.

Let W and W' be distinct $(n-1)$-spaces. The common neighbours of W and W' are the 1-spaces contained in $W \cap W'$. Now $W + W'$ has dimension n, so $W \cap W'$ is an $(n-2)$-space. The number of 1-spaces contained in an $(n-2)$-space is $\binom{n-2}{1}_q$.

Similarly, let W and W' be distinct 1-spaces. The common neighbours of W and W' are the $(n-1)$-spaces containing $W + W'$. This is a 2-space, since $W \cap W'$ is 0-dimensional. The number of $(n-1)$-spaces containing a given 2-space is $\binom{n-2}{1}_q$. □

The case $n = 3$ is especially important.

Example 4.12. The incidence graph $I_3(q)$ is an extremal design graph, of half-size $m = q^2 + q + 1$ and degree $d = q + 1$. The incidence graph $I_3(2)$ is the Heawood graph.

Assume now that V is endowed with a scalar product. Proposition 4.9 provides a bijection between the $(n-1)$-spaces and the 1-spaces of V. Using this bijection, we can give an alternate, and somewhat simpler, description of $I_n(q)$. Take two copies of the set of 1-spaces, that is, lines through the origin, and join a 'black' line to a 'white' line whenever they are orthogonal. Note that the orthogonal picture is independent of the choice of scalar product, for it agrees with the original incidence picture.

The orthogonal picture of $I_n(q)$ admits two concrete realizations that are worth emphasizing. They yield, in particular, two facts about $I_n(q)$ that are not obvious from the incidence picture.

Firstly, let V be $\mathbb{F}^n$, equipped with the standard scalar product. Let us view $\mathbb{F}^n$ as the subspace of $\mathbb{F}^{n+1}$ with vanishing last coordinate. Then the lines of $\mathbb{F}^n$ are also lines in $\mathbb{F}^{n+1}$, and they are orthogonal in $\mathbb{F}^n$ if and only if they are orthogonal in $\mathbb{F}^{n+1}$. So the following holds:

Proposition 4.13. The graph $I_n(q)$ is an induced subgraph of $I_{n+1}(q)$.

The lines through the origin in $\mathbb{F}^n$ are parameterized by non-zero vectors in $\mathbb{F}^n$ modulo scalars. So, somewhat more algebraically, $I_n(q)$ is the bipartite graph on two copies of the quotient space $\mathbb{F}^n \setminus \{0\}$ mod $\mathbb{F}^*$, in which two coloured projective vectors $[x_1, \ldots, x_n]_{\bullet}$ and $[y_1, \ldots, y_n]_{\circ}$ are joined whenever $x_1 y_1 + \cdots + x_n y_n = 0$.

Secondly, let V be $\mathbb{K}$, an extension of $\mathbb{F}$ of degree n, endowed with the tracial scalar product. Here, the lines through the origin can be identified with the quotient multiplicative group $\mathbb{K}^*/\mathbb{F}^*$. So we may think of $I_n(q)$ as the bipartite graph on two copies of $\mathbb{K}^*/\mathbb{F}^*$, with an edge joining $[a]_{\bullet}$ to $[b]_{\circ}$ whenever $\text{Tr}(ab) = 0$. In other words, we have the following proposition:

Proposition 4.14. Let $\mathbb{K}$ be an extension of $\mathbb{F}$ of degree n. Then $I_n(q)$ is the bi-Cayley graph of the quotient group $\mathbb{K}^*/\mathbb{F}^*$, with respect to the subset $\{[s] : \text{Tr}(s) = 0\}$.

Since the quotient group $\mathbb{K}^*/\mathbb{F}^*$ is cyclic, we deduce the following:

Corollary 4.15. $I_n(q)$ is a Cayley graph of the dihedral group of order $2(q^n-1)/(q-1)$.

Exercise 4.16. Let q be, as usual, a power of a prime. Show that the cyclic group $G = \mathbb{Z}_{q^2+q+1}$ contains a *perfect difference set*, that is, a subset $S \subseteq G$ with the property that every non-zero element of G can be expressed, in a unique way, as the difference of two elements of S.

Notes. Example 4.12 addresses the problem of constructing extremal design graphs, and it says that there are 'standard' examples in degree $q + 1$, for each prime power q. Are there any other examples? It turns out that there are non-standard examples in degree $q + 1$, for each $q \geq 9$ which is a prime power but not a prime. The constructions are, again, of algebraic nature. However, there are no known examples, and there are probably none, in degree $n + 1$, when n is not a prime power! This is, up to a slight reformulation, one of the most famous problems in combinatorics. The common formulation concerns combinatorial objects known as *finite projective planes*. Extremal design graphs are the incidence graphs of finite projective planes. A beautiful theorem of Bruck and Ryser says the following: if there are extremal design graphs of degree $n + 1$, and $n \equiv 1, 2$ mod 4, then n is the sum of two squares. For example, the Bruck–Ryser criterion implies that there are no examples in degree 7, but it says nothing about the case of degree 11. In 1989, after massive computer calculations, it was eventually shown that there are no examples in degree 11. Or was it? See Lam (*The search for a finite projective plane of order 10*, Amer. Math. Monthly 1991; Zbl0744.51011).

Exercise 4.16 and the idea underlying Proposition 4.14 are due to Singer (*A theorem in finite projective geometry and some applications to number theory*, Trans. Amer. Math. Soc. 1938; Zbl 0019.00502). Quite interestingly, Exercise 4.16 is a group-theoretic statement proved by a finite-field perspective.

5

Squares in finite fields

The previous chapter was concerned, for the most part, with linear algebra *over* a finite field. In this chapter, we mostly work *within* a finite field $\mathbb{F}$ with q elements. Throughout, we assume that q is odd.

5.1 The quadratic character

The squaring homomorphism $\mathbb{F}^* \to \mathbb{F}^*$, given by $x \mapsto x^2$, is two-to-one: $x^2 = y^2$ if and only if $x = \pm y$. So half the elements of $\mathbb{F}^*$ are squares, and half are not. The *quadratic character* $\sigma : \mathbb{F}^* \to \{\pm 1\}$ is given by

$$\sigma(a) = \begin{cases} 1 & \text{if } a \text{ is a square in } \mathbb{F}^*, \\ -1 & \text{if } a \text{ is not a square in } \mathbb{F}^*. \end{cases}$$

Theorem 5.1. The quadratic character σ is multiplicative on $\mathbb{F}^*$, and it is explicitly given by the *Euler formula*

$$\sigma(a) = a^{(q-1)/2}.$$

Proof. Let $\tau(a) = a^{(q-1)/2}$ for $a \in \mathbb{F}^*$. Note that $\tau(a) = \pm 1$, as $\tau(a)^2 = a^{q-1} = 1$. Note also that τ does take the value -1, for otherwise the equation $X^{(q-1)/2} = 1$ would have too many solutions in $\mathbb{F}$. Thus $\tau : \mathbb{F}^* \to \{\pm 1\}$ is an onto homomorphism. Its kernel has size $\frac{1}{2}(q-1)$, and it contains the non-zero squares, whose number is also $\frac{1}{2}(q-1)$. Therefore the kernel of τ consists precisely of the non-zero squares. In other words, $\tau(a) = 1$ if a is a square in $\mathbb{F}^*$, and $\tau(a) = -1$ if a is not a square in $\mathbb{F}^*$, that is, $\tau = \sigma$. $\qquad\square$

The question of whether -1 is a square or not is an important one. An application of Euler's formula yields the following.

Corollary 5.2. -1 is a square in $\mathbb{F}$ if and only if $q \equiv 1 \bmod 4$.

If $\mathbb{K}$ is an extension of $\mathbb{F}$, how is being a square in $\mathbb{F}$ related to being a square in $\mathbb{K}$? This question too can be settled by applying Euler's formula. Let n denote the degree of the extension $\mathbb{K}/\mathbb{F}$. Then for each $a \in \mathbb{F}^*$ we have

$$\sigma_{\mathbb{K}}(a) = a^{(q^n-1)/2} = \sigma_{\mathbb{F}}(a)^{1+q+\cdots+q^{n-1}} = \sigma_{\mathbb{F}}(a)^n.$$

Thus, the following holds:

Corollary 5.3. If $\mathbb{K}$ is an extension of even degree, then all elements of $\mathbb{F}$ are squares in $\mathbb{K}$. If $\mathbb{K}$ is an extension of odd degree, then an element of $\mathbb{F}$ is a square in $\mathbb{K}$ if and only if it is already a square in $\mathbb{F}$.

There are as many squares as non-squares in $\mathbb{F}^*$, so

$$\sum_{a \in \mathbb{F}^*} \sigma(a) = 0.$$

The quadratic character σ is extended to $\mathbb{F}$ by setting $\sigma(0) = 0$. With this convention, σ continues to be multiplicative and to satisfy the Euler formula. The above summation formula holds over $\mathbb{F}$ as well.

The next lemma is a computation involving the quadratic character. We will use it as an ingredient in proving several interesting results.

Lemma 5.4. We have

$$\sum_{a+b=c} \sigma(a)\sigma(b) = \begin{cases} -\sigma(-1) & \text{if } c \neq 0, \\ \sigma(-1)(q-1) & \text{if } c = 0. \end{cases}$$

Proof. Put $J_c := \sum_{a+b=c} \sigma(a)\sigma(b)$. For $c = 0$, we have

$$J_0 = \sum_a \sigma(a)\sigma(-a) = \sigma(-1)(q-1)$$

since $\sigma(a)\sigma(-a) = \sigma(-1)$ for each $a \in \mathbb{F}^*$. For $c \neq 0$, the change of variables $a \mapsto ca$, $b \mapsto cb$ yields

$$\sum_{a+b=c} \sigma(a)\sigma(b) = \sum_{a+b=1} \sigma(ca)\sigma(cb) = \sum_{a+b=1} \sigma(a)\sigma(b).$$

That is to say, $J_c = J_1$ for all $c \neq 0$. To compute the value of J_1, we observe that

$$\sum_c J_c = \left(\sum_a \sigma(a) \right)\left(\sum_b \sigma(b) \right) = 0.$$

Therefore $J_0 + (q-1)J_1 = 0$, and it follows that $J_1 = -\sigma(-1)$.   □

Our first use of Lemma 5.4 concerns the equation $aX^2 + bY^2 = 1$, for $a, b \in \mathbb{F}^*$. A simple counting argument shows that the equation is solvable in $\mathbb{F}$: the two subsets $\{ax^2 : x \in \mathbb{F}\}$ and $\{1 - by^2 : y \in \mathbb{F}\}$ have size $\frac{1}{2}(q+1)$, so they must intersect. But thanks to Lemma 5.4, we can actually count the number of solutions.

Proposition 5.5. The equation $aX^2 + bY^2 = 1$ has $q - \sigma(-ab) = q \pm 1$ solutions. In particular, the equation $X^2 + Y^2 = c$ has $q - \sigma(-1)$ solutions, for every $c \in \mathbb{F}^*$.

First proof. Let $N(f)$ denote the number of solutions in $\mathbb{F}$ of a polynomial equation $f = 0$. Note that $N(X^2 - c) = 1 + \sigma(c)$; more generally, $N(aX^2 - c) = 1 + \sigma(ac)$ for $a \neq 0$. Then

$$N(aX^2 + bY^2 - 1) = \sum_{r+s=1} N(aX^2 - r)N(bY^2 - s)$$

$$= \sum_{r+s=1} \left(1 + \sigma(ar)\right)\left(1 + \sigma(bs)\right).$$

We have

$$\sum_{r+s=1} 1 = q, \qquad \sum_{r+s=1} \sigma(r) = \sum_{r+s=1} \sigma(s) = 0,$$

so we get

$$N(aX^2 + bY^2 - 1) = q + \sigma(ab) \sum_{r+s=1} \sigma(r)\sigma(s) = q - \sigma(-ab).$$

The second part follows by taking $a = b = 1/c$. $\qquad\qquad\qquad\qquad\qquad$ □

Let us also record an alternative proof, which does not appeal to Lemma 5.4.

Second proof. Dividing the equation $aX^2 + bY^2 = 1$ by a, and setting $d = -b/a$, $c = 1/a$, we reach the equation $X^2 - dY^2 = c$. We wish to show that, for each $d \in \mathbb{F}^*$, the latter equation has $q - \sigma(d)$ solutions independently of $c \in \mathbb{F}^*$.

Consider the case when d is a square. After writing $d = d_0^2$ for some $d_0 \in \mathbb{F}^*$, the equation $X^2 - dY^2 = c$ becomes $(X + d_0Y)(X - d_0Y) = c$. This, in turn, is equivalent to solving the system

$$X + d_0Y = s, \quad X - d_0Y = cs^{-1},$$

for each $s \in \mathbb{F}^*$. This system has a unique solution, namely $x = (s + cs^{-1})/2$ and $y = d_0^{-1}(s - cs^{-1})/2$. Note here that division by 2 is allowed, since the characteristic is odd. We conclude that, in this case, $X^2 - dY^2 = c$ has $q - 1$ solutions.

Consider now the case when d is not a square. Let $\mathbb{K} = \mathbb{F}[X]/(X^2 - d)$ be the quadratic extension of $\mathbb{F}$ discussed in Example 4.5. Then the solutions of $X^2 - dY^2 = c$ correspond, via $(x, y) \mapsto x + y\sqrt{d}$, to the elements of $\mathbb{K}^*$ having norm c. Since the norm map is an onto homomorphism from $\mathbb{K}^*$ to $\mathbb{F}^*$, there are $|\mathbb{K}^*|/|\mathbb{F}^*| = (q^2 - 1)/(q - 1) = q + 1$ such elements for each c. To conclude, $X^2 - dY^2 = c$ has $q + 1$ solutions in this case. $\qquad\qquad\qquad\qquad\qquad$ □

Exercise 5.6. Find the number of solutions to the equation $X_1^2 + \cdots + X_n^2 = c$, where $c \in \mathbb{F}$.

5.2 Quadratic reciprocity

Lemma 5.7 (Gauss). Let p be an odd prime, and let $\zeta \in \mathbb{C}$ be a pth root of unity. Then the cyclotomic integer

$$G = \sum_{a \in \mathbb{Z}_p} \sigma(a)\zeta^a \in \mathbb{Z}[\zeta]$$

satisfies $G^2 = \sigma(-1)p$.

Proof. We have $\zeta^p = 1$, so $\sum_{c \in \mathbb{Z}_p} \zeta^c = 1 + \zeta + \cdots + \zeta^{p-1} = 0$. Using Lemma 5.4 along the way, we compute

$$G^2 = \sum_{a,b} \sigma(a)\sigma(b)\zeta^{a+b} = \sum_c \left(\sum_{a+b=c} \sigma(a)\sigma(b) \right)\zeta^c$$

$$= \sigma(-1)(p-1) - \sigma(-1)\left(\sum_{c \neq 0} \zeta^c \right) = \sigma(-1)p,$$

as desired.   □

Gauss's lemma is, well, just a lemma, so we might guess that something bigger lurks around the corner. Indeed, it is the law of quadratic reciprocity.

Theorem 5.8 (Euler, Legendre, Gauss). Let p and ℓ be distinct odd primes. If $p \equiv 1$ mod 4 or $\ell \equiv 1$ mod 4, then p is a square mod ℓ if and only if ℓ is a square mod p. If $p, \ell \equiv 3$ mod 4, then p is a square mod ℓ if and only if ℓ is not a square mod p.

The *Legendre symbol* for an odd prime p is defined as

$$(a/p) = \begin{cases} 1 & \text{if } a \text{ is a square mod } p, \\ -1 & \text{if } a \text{ is not a square mod } p, \end{cases}$$

when a is an integer relatively prime to p, respectively $(a/p) = 0$ when a is an integer divisible by p. Clearly, (a/p) depends only on the residue class a mod p. In terms of the Legendre symbol, the law of quadratic reciprocity can be compactly stated as follows: for distinct odd primes p and ℓ we have

$$(p/\ell)(\ell/p) = (-1)^{(p-1)(\ell-1)/4}. \tag{QR}$$

A convenient reformulation, especially for the proofs below, is

$$(\ell/p) = (p^*/\ell), \quad \text{where } p^* = (-1/p)p. \tag{QR*}$$

Indeed, $(-1/p) = (-1)^{(p-1)/2}$ so $((-1/p)/\ell) = (-1)^{(p-1)(\ell-1)/4}$.

Proof of Theorem 5.8. Let G be defined as in the previous lemma, with respect to p. We compute G^ℓ mod ℓ in two ways. On the one hand, we have

$$G^\ell = \Big(\sum_{a \in \mathbb{Z}_p} (a/p)\zeta^a \Big)^\ell \equiv \sum_{a \in \mathbb{Z}_p} \big((a/p)\zeta^a \big)^\ell \quad \text{mod } \ell$$

and

$$\sum_{a \in \mathbb{Z}_p} \big((a/p)\zeta^a \big)^\ell = \sum_{a \in \mathbb{Z}_p} (a/p)\zeta^{a\ell} = \sum_{a \in \mathbb{Z}_p} (a\ell^{-1}/p)\zeta^a = (\ell/p)G.$$

In short, $G^\ell \equiv (\ell/p)G$ mod ℓ.

On the other hand, by Gauss's lemma we may write

$$G^{\ell-1} = (G^2)^{(\ell-1)/2} = (p^*)^{(\ell-1)/2}$$

and

$$(p^*)^{(\ell-1)/2} \equiv (p^*/\ell) \quad \text{mod } \ell$$

by Euler's formula. It follows that $G^\ell \equiv (p^*/\ell)G$ mod ℓ.

The two congruences for G^ℓ imply that $(\ell/p) = (p^*/\ell)$. Otherwise, we would have $G \equiv -G$, that is, $2G \equiv 0$ mod ℓ. Squaring, and using Gauss's lemma once again, leads to $4p \equiv 0$ mod ℓ. This is a congruence in the cyclotomic ring $\mathbb{Z}[\zeta]$, and it means that $4p = \ell(c_0 + c_1\zeta + \cdots + c_{p-1}\zeta^{p-1})$ for some integers $c_0, c_1, \ldots, c_{p-1}$. Since the minimal polynomial of ζ is $X^{p-1} + \cdots + X + 1$, it follows that $\ell c_0 = \ell c_1 = \cdots = \ell c_{p-1} - 4p$. Whence $4p \equiv 0$ mod ℓ in $\mathbb{Z}$, and this is a contradiction. $\square$

The law of quadratic reciprocity is complemented by the following: if p is an odd prime, then 2 is a square mod p if and only if $p \equiv \pm 1$ mod 8. This can be proved by looking at $(1 + i)^p$ mod p in two different ways. The details are left to the reader.

Exercise 5.9. Let p and ℓ be distinct odd primes. Give a different proof for the law of quadratic reciprocity, $(\ell/p) = (p^*/\ell)$, by arguing as follows. Let N denote the number of solutions to the equation $X_1^2 + \cdots + X_\ell^2 = 1$ in $\mathbb{Z}_p$. Show that $N \equiv 1 + (p^*/\ell)$ mod ℓ, but also $N \equiv 1 + (\ell/p)$ mod ℓ.

Notes. Quadratic reciprocity played a fundamental role in the history of number theory. Euler discovered the square laws experimentally, and he was able to prove the complementary laws concerning $(-1/p)$ and $(2/p)$. Legendre had a partial proof of the quadratic reciprocity law, a name that he introduced, along with the notation that we now call the Legendre symbol. In the course of his investigations, Legendre also put forth the claim that there are infinitely many primes congruent to a mod b, for every pair of relatively prime integers a and b. This is a fact that we now know as Dirichlet's theorem. The first complete proof of the quadratic reciprocity law is due to Gauss, and so is the second, the third, the fourth, the fifth, and the sixth —

all essentially different. He added two more proofs later on. More than 200 proofs of the quadratic reciprocity law have been published by now. The one suggested in Exercise 5.9 is due to V.-A. Lebesgue.

5.3 Paley graphs

We usually view the non-zero squares of $\mathbb{F}$ in a multiplicative light, but we will now take an additive perspective. The fact that the equation $X^2 + Y^2 = c$ is solvable for each $c \in \mathbb{F}^*$ means that every element in $\mathbb{F}^*$ is the sum of at most two non-zero squares. As for 0, it is the sum of two non-zero squares precisely when $q \equiv 1$ mod 4. If $q \equiv 3$ mod 4, then 0 is the sum of three non-zero squares, since -1 is the sum of two non-zero squares. In particular, the set of non-zero squares $(\mathbb{F}^*)^2$ is an additive generating set for $\mathbb{F}$. On the other hand, $(\mathbb{F}^*)^2$ is additively symmetric, that is, $(\mathbb{F}^*)^2 = -(\mathbb{F}^*)^2$, if and only if $q \equiv 1$ mod 4. These considerations motivate the following definition.

For $q \equiv 1$ mod 4, the *Paley graph* $P(q)$ is the Cayley graph of the additive group of $\mathbb{F}$ with respect to the set of non-zero squares $(\mathbb{F}^*)^2$.

Theorem 5.10. The Paley graph $P(q)$ is strongly regular, with parameters

$$n = q, \qquad d = \tfrac{1}{2}(q-1), \qquad a = \tfrac{1}{4}(q-5), \qquad c = \tfrac{1}{4}(q-1).$$

Recall, a and c denote the number of common neighbours shared by any two adjacent vertices, respectively any two non-adjacent vertices.

Proof. The size and the degree of $P(q)$ are immediate. Now let v and w be distinct vertices. The number of common neighbours is the number of representations of $v - w$ as an ordered sum of two non-zero squares in $\mathbb{F}$. By Proposition 5.5, there are $q - 1$ pairs $(x, y) \in \mathbb{F} \times \mathbb{F}$ satisfying $x^2 + y^2 = v - w$. If $v - w$ is not a square (i.e., v and w are not adjacent) then both x and y are non-zero, and $v - w$ is the sum of two non-zero squares in $\tfrac{1}{4}(q-1)$ ordered ways. If $v - w$ is a square (i.e., v and w are adjacent) then there are two solutions when $x = 0$ and two solutions when $y = 0$, hence $q - 5$ solutions for which both x and y are non-zero. Thus $v - w$ is the sum of two non-zero squares in $\tfrac{1}{4}(q-5)$ ordered ways. $\qquad\square$

The first in the sequence of Paley graphs, $P(5)$, is the cycle C_5. The next one, $P(9)$, is the product $K_3 \times K_3$. A very keen reader might notice that the Paley parameters agree with the parameters of the strongly regular graphs constructed in Theorem 3.22 in one case: $P(25)$. We leave it as an exercise for that reader to check that $P(25)$ is, indeed, isomorphic to X_G for $G = \mathbb{Z}_5$.

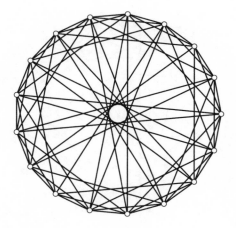

Figure 5.1. The Paley graph $P(17)$.

The field $\mathbb{F}$ has permutations coming from its two operations, and it is instructive to know their effect on the graph $P(q)$. The translation $+t : \mathbb{F} \to \mathbb{F}$ by $t \in \mathbb{F}$ is, of course, a graph automorphism. More interesting is the scaling $\times r : \mathbb{F} \to \mathbb{F}$ by $r \in \mathbb{F}^*$. When r is a square, this is a graph automorphism fixing the vertex 0. When r is a non-square, we get a 'switch' changing edges to non-edges, respectively non-edges to edges.

Exercise 5.11. The *Ramsey number* $R(k)$ is the smallest number with the property that, in any group of $R(k)$ persons, either there are k of them who know each other, or there are k of them who do not know each other. Show that $R(4) \geq 18$.

Here is a further fact concerning Paley graphs.

Proposition 5.12. The Paley graph $P(q^2)$ has chromatic number q, and independence number q.

Proof. Firstly, note that $q^2 \equiv 1 \bmod 4$, so we may indeed consider $P(q^2)$. Let $\mathbb{K}$ be a field with q^2 elements, and let $\mathbb{F}$ be a subfield with q elements. Every element of $\mathbb{F}$ is a square in $\mathbb{K}$, so $\mathbb{F}$ defines a complete subgraph of $P(q^2)$. It follows that $\mathrm{chr}\, P(q^2) \geq q$. Moreover, we may partition the elements of $\mathbb{K}$ into q cosets of $\mathbb{F}$, and each such coset C forms a complete subgraph of $P(q^2)$. Hence $\mathrm{ind}\, P(q^2) \leq q$.

Now let r be a non-square in $\mathbb{K}$. Then $r\mathbb{F}$ is an independent subset of $P(q^2)$, so $\mathrm{ind}\, P(q^2) \geq q$. Actually rC is an independent subset for every coset C as before. Painting each rC monochromatically shows that $\mathrm{chr}\, P(q^2) \leq q$. $\qquad\square$

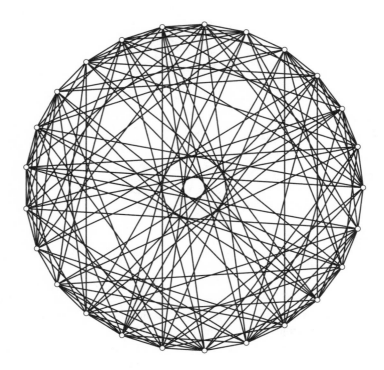

Figure 5.2. The Paley graph $P(25)$.

For $q \equiv 3 \bmod 4$, we can no longer use a Cayley graph construction. We define the *bi-Paley graph* $BP(q)$ as the bi-Cayley graph of the additive group of $\mathbb{F}$ with respect to the non-zero squares $(\mathbb{F}^*)^2$.

We discard $BP(3)$, as it is rather degenerate, namely, it is the disjoint union of three copies of K_2. So the first graph of the bi-Paley family is $BP(7)$, which turns out to be the Heawood graph.

Theorem 5.13. The bi-Paley graph $BP(q)$ is a design graph, with parameters

$$m = q, \qquad d = \tfrac{1}{2}(q-1), \qquad c = \tfrac{1}{4}(q-3).$$

Proof. The half-size m and the degree d are obvious. We check the design property: two vertices of the same colour have $c = \tfrac{1}{4}(q-3)$ common neighbours. It suffices to argue the case of two distinct black vertices, $v_\bullet$ and $w_\bullet$. The number of white vertices adjacent to both $v_\bullet$ and $w_\bullet$ is the number of representations of $v - w$ as the difference of two non-zero squares in $\mathbb{F}$. There are $q - 1$ pairs $(x, y) \in \mathbb{F} \times \mathbb{F}$ satisfying $x^2 - y^2 = v - w$.

Now observe that $(\mathbb{F}^*)^2$ and $-(\mathbb{F}^*)^2$ partition $\mathbb{F}^*$, as -1 is not a square. If $v - w$ is a non-zero square then necessarily $x \neq 0$, and there are two solutions with $y = 0$. Thus $v - w$ is the difference of two squares in $\frac{1}{4}(q - 3)$ ways. If $w - v$ is a non-zero square then $y \neq 0$, and there are two solutions with $x = 0$. Again, $v - w$ is the difference of two squares in $\frac{1}{4}(q - 3)$ ways.   □

We note that the bi-Paley graph $BP(q)$ is not a bipartite double. The parity obstruction is effective here: both $m = q$ and $d = \frac{1}{2}(q - 1)$ are odd, as $q \equiv 3 \bmod 4$.

Notes. Paley graphs are named after Raymond Paley, who used the quadratic character to construct Hadamard matrices. These are square matrices whose entries are ± 1, and whose rows are orthogonal. The graph-theoretic implementation of the same idea came much later.

Ramsey numbers are named after Frank Ramsey. It is actually the case, and not too difficult to prove, that $R(4) = 18$. Showing that $R(3) = 6$ is easy. It is, however, rather striking that the value of $R(5)$ is not known! The best available knowledge at the time of writing is that $43 \leq R(5) \leq 49$.

5.4 A comparison

We have defined two families of design graphs from finite fields. For a prime power $q \equiv 3 \bmod 4$, the bi-Paley graph $BP(q)$ has parameters

$$(m, d, c) = \left(q, \frac{q - 1}{2}, \frac{q - 3}{4} \right).$$

The incidence graph $I_n(q)$, where $n \geq 3$ and q is an arbitrary prime power, has parameters

$$(m, d, c) = \left(\frac{q^n - 1}{q - 1}, \frac{q^{n-1} - 1}{q - 1}, \frac{q^{n-2} - 1}{q - 1} \right).$$

We wish to compare these two families, and we start by comparing their parameters.

Proposition 5.14. The parameters of a bi-Paley graph and those of an incidence graph agree only for $BP(q)$ and $I_n(2)$, where $q = 2^n - 1$ is a prime.

Proof. A bi-Paley graph satisfies $m = 2d + 1$. Imposing this relation on an incidence graph $I_n(q')$, we find that $q' = 2$. The parameters of $I_n(2)$ are $(2^n - 1, 2^{n-1} - 1, 2^{n-2} - 1)$, and these are the parameters of a bi-Paley graph precisely when $2^n - 1$ is a prime power. Note here that $2^n - 1 \equiv 3 \bmod 4$, as $n \geq 3$.

We are left with arguing that $2^n - 1$ is a prime power if and only if $2^n - 1$ is actually a prime. So let $2^n - 1 = p^d$, where p is a prime and d is a positive integer that we claim to be 1. As $2^n - 1 \equiv 3 \bmod 4$, we first deduce that d is odd. We can then write $2^n = p^d + 1 = (p + 1)(p^{d-1} - \cdots + 1)$. But the latter factor is odd, since both p and d are odd, so it has to equal 1. Therefore $2^n - 1 = p$.   □

The prime sequence that appears in the previous proposition is in fact a notorious one. A prime of the form $2^n - 1$ is known as a *Mersenne prime*. Note that n is, a fortiori, prime as well. Very few Mersenne primes are known: at the time of writing, the 49th has just been found. The sequence of primes n that yield a Mersenne prime starts with $2, 3, 5, 7, 13, 17, 19, 31, 61, 89$. It could be that there are infinitely many Mersenne primes.

Next, we consider possible isomorphisms between the two families. The graphs $BP(q)$ and $I_n(2)$ are isomorphic for the first allowed values, $q = 7$ respectively $n = 3$. This can be seen in several ways. One is simply by drawing: both turn out to be the Heawood graph. The following exercise suggests a more sophisticated approach.

Exercise 5.15. Show that the bi-Paley graph $BP(7)$ is isomorphic to the incidence graph $I_3(2)$ by employing the notion of a bi-Cayley graph isomorphism.

It turns out that there is no other isomorphism between bi-Paley graphs and incidence graphs.

Theorem 5.16. Let $q \equiv 3 \bmod 4$, and $q > 7$. Then the bi-Paley graph $BP(q)$ is not isomorphic to any incidence graph $I_n(q')$.

To see the somewhat subtle difference, let us take a closer look at the design property in incidence graphs. Thinking of $I_n(q')$ in the incidence picture, consider two lines and the hyperplanes containing them. Then these hyperplanes contain the entire plane spanned by the two lines, so they contain $q'-1$ additional lines. Dually, if we take two hyperplanes and the lines that they contain, then these lines are contained in $q'-1$ further hyperplanes. One way to phrase this is that an incidence graph is a design graph in which we cannot recover a pair of monochromatic vertices from its joint neighbours. The proof of the theorem consists in showing that the contrary holds in bi-Paley graphs — with the exception of $BP(7)$.

Proof. We claim that, for $q > 7$, the bi-Paley graph $BP(q)$ has the following property: any two distinct vertices of the same colour are determined by their $\frac{1}{4}(q-3)$ common neighbours. Arguing by contradiction, let us assume that there are three distinct vertices of the same colour sharing $\frac{1}{4}(q-3)$ common neighbours. In terms of the underlying field $\mathbb{F}$, this means that there are three distinct elements a, b, and c, and a subset $S \subseteq \mathbb{F}$ of size $\frac{1}{4}(q-3)$, such that $x-a$, $x-b$, are $x-c$ are non-zero squares whenever $x \in S$.

Let S_a be the subset of all $x \in \mathbb{F} \setminus S$ so that $x-a$ is a non-zero square. Graphically, the subset S_a underlies the neighbours of a that are not shared with b and c. Define

S_b and S_c similarly. The design property implies that S_a, S_b, and S_c are mutually disjoint, and a degree count gives

$$|S_a| = |S_b| = |S_c| = \tfrac{1}{4}(q + 1).$$

As $|S| + |S_a| + |S_b| + |S_c| = q = |\mathbb{F}|$, it follows that S, S_a, S_b, S_c form a partition of $\mathbb{F}$. This means that precisely one of the following occurs for any $x \neq a, b, c$:

   $(x \in S)$ $x-a$, $x-b$, are $x-c$ are squares;
   $(x \in S_a)$ $x-a$ is a square, but $x-b$ and $x-c$ are not;
   $(x \in S_b)$ $x-b$ is a square, but $x-a$ and $x-c$ are not;
   $(x \in S_c)$ $x-c$ is a square, but $x-a$ and $x-b$ are not.

This means that $f(x) = (x - a)(x - b)(x - c)$ is a square, possibly 0, for all $x \in \mathbb{F}$. We reach a contradiction in light of the lemma below.   □

Lemma 5.17. Let $f \in \mathbb{F}[X]$ be a cubic polynomial. If $q > 9$, then some value of f is a non-square.

Proof. Assume, on the contrary, that every value of f is a square. Then the polynomial $f(f^{(q-1)/2} - 1) = f^{(q+1)/2} - f$ takes only the zero value. But the same holds for the polynomial $P = X^q - X$. A non-zero polynomial vanishing on $\mathbb{F}$ cannot have degree smaller than q so, using division with remainder, it must be divisible by P. Write

$$f^{(q+1)/2} - f = Ph,$$

where $h \in \mathbb{F}[X]$ has degree $\tfrac{1}{2}(q + 3)$. Taking the formal derivative, we get

$$\frac{q + 1}{2} f' f^{(q-1)/2} - f' = Ph' + P'h = Ph' - h.$$

Now the mod P congruences

$$f^{(q+1)/2} \equiv f, \qquad \frac{q + 1}{2} f' f^{(q-1)/2} \equiv f' - h$$

imply that

$$\frac{q - 1}{2} f'f + hf \equiv 0.$$

So the degree of the above polynomial, $\tfrac{1}{2}(q + 3) + 3$, has to be at least $\deg(P) = q$. Thus $q \leq 9$, a contradiction.   □

Notes. Zannier (*Polynomials modulo p whose values are squares (elementary improvements on some consequences of Weil's bounds*), Enseign. Math. 1998; Zbl 1064.11501) gives an elementary argument for the following basic fact from the theory of elliptic curves over finite fields: the equation $y^2 = f(x)$, where f is a cubic polynomial, has solutions for $q > 3$. After rescaling f by a non-square, Lemma 5.17 says that $y^2 = f(x)$ has a solution with $y \neq 0$ for $q > 9$. The proof of Lemma 5.17 adapts Zannier's nice argument.

6

Characters

We start with a general discussion of characters on finite abelian groups. Then we discuss character sums over finite fields.

6.1 Characters of finite abelian groups

Let G be a finite abelian group, whose operation is written multiplicatively. A *character* χ of G is a group homomorphism $\chi : G \to \mathbb{C}^*$.

Example 6.1. Let $\mathbb{F}$ be a finite field of odd characteristic. Then the quadratic character σ is a character of the multiplicative group $\mathbb{F}^*$.

Example 6.2. On the additive group $\mathbb{Z}_n$, a list of n different characters is given by

$$\chi_k(a) = e^{2\pi i k a/n}, \quad k = 0, \ldots, n-1.$$

Example 6.3. On the additive group $(\mathbb{Z}_2)^n$, a list of 2^n different characters is given by

$$\chi_I(v) = (-1)^{\sum_{i \in I} v_i}, \quad I \subseteq \{1, \ldots, n\}.$$

The characters of G take values in the unit circle $\{z : |z| = 1\}$. In fact, the values are roots of unity of order $|G|$. Let $G^\wedge$ denote the set of characters of G. Then $G^\wedge$ is a group under pointwise multiplication, the neutral element being the trivial character $\mathbb{1}$ defined by $g \mapsto 1$ for all $g \in G$. The inverse of a character χ is the conjugate character $\overline{\chi}$. The finite abelian group $G^\wedge$ is called the *dual* of G.

Theorem 6.4. *The dual $G^\wedge$ is isomorphic to G. In particular, G has exactly $|G|$ characters.*

Proof. This follows by combining three facts: G is isomorphic to a direct product of finite cyclic groups; taking duals is compatible with direct products, in the sense that $(G_1 \times G_2)^\wedge$ is isomorphic to $G_1^\wedge \times G_2^\wedge$; if G is a finite cyclic group, then $G^\wedge$ is isomorphic to G. The detailed verification is left to the reader. $\square$

An immediate consequence is that G admits a non-trivial character which is real valued, if and only if $|G|$ is even. Indeed, a character χ is real valued and non-trivial precisely when its values are ± 1. Equivalently, χ has order 2 in the dual group $G^\wedge$, and such a character exists if and only if $|G^\wedge| = |G|$ is even. A related observation is that, in Example 6.1, the quadratic character σ is the unique real-valued, non-trivial character on $\mathbb{F}^*$. The reason is that the cyclic group $\mathbb{F}^*$ contains a unique element of order 2.

Character theory for finite abelian groups is grounded on two facts. One is the previous theorem, and the other is the following fundamental relation for non-trivial characters.

Theorem 6.5. If χ is a non-trivial character of G, then

$$\sum_{g \in G} \chi(g) = 0.$$

Proof. For each $h \in G$ we have

$$\chi(h) \sum_{g \in G} \chi(g) = \sum_{g \in G} \chi(hg) = \sum_{g \in G} \chi(g).$$

As χ is non-trivial, there exists $h \in G$ with $\chi(h) \neq 1$. The desired relation follows. □

We deduce, in sequence, several consequences. The first concerns the way in which characters sit in $\ell^2 G$. This is the finite-dimensional space of complex-valued functions on G, endowed with the usual inner product,

$$\langle \phi, \psi \rangle = \sum_{g \in G} \phi(g)\overline{\psi(g)}.$$

Corollary 6.6. The characters of G form an orthogonal basis of $\ell^2 G$.

Proof. If χ_1 and χ_2 are distinct characters of G, then

$$\langle \chi_1, \chi_2 \rangle = \sum_{g \in G} \chi_1(g)\overline{\chi_2}(g) = \sum_{g \in G} (\chi_1\overline{\chi_2})(g) = 0$$

as $\chi_1\overline{\chi_2}$ is a non-trivial character. Thus, the characters are orthogonal. As there are $|G| = \dim \ell^2 G$ characters, we conclude that they form a basis. □

Corollary 6.7. The characters of G distinguish the elements of G. Namely, if $g \neq 1$ is a non-trivial element in G, then there exists a character χ such that $\chi(g) \neq 1$.

Proof. Let $\mathbb{1}_g : G \to \mathbb{C}$ denote the characteristic function of g. By the previous result, $\mathbb{1}_g$ is a linear combination of characters, say $\mathbb{1}_g = \sum a_\chi \chi$. Evaluating both sides at g, respectively at 1, we obtain

$$1 = \sum a_\chi \chi(g), \qquad 0 = \sum a_\chi.$$

So there must be some χ satisfying $\chi(g) \neq 1$. □

Corollary 6.8. If $g \neq 1$ is a non-trivial element in G, then

$$\sum_{\chi \in G^\wedge} \chi(g) = 0.$$

Proof. The identity to be proved is the dual of the fundamental character sum, and we will use the dual trick. Thanks to Corollary 6.7, there is a character χ' of G satisfying $\chi'(g) \neq 1$. Then

$$\chi'(g) \sum_{\chi \in G^\wedge} \chi(g) = \sum_{\chi \in G^\wedge} (\chi'\chi)(g) = \sum_{\chi \in G^\wedge} \chi(g),$$

and the claimed relation follows.   □

Exercise 6.9. Let d be a positive integer, and $g \in G$. Then

$$\sum_{\chi^d = 1} \chi(g) = \left|\{h \in G : h^d = g\}\right|.$$

6.2 Character sums over finite fields

The characters of a finite field $\mathbb{F}$ come in two flavours: characters of the additive group $(\mathbb{F}, +)$, and characters of the multiplicative group $(\mathbb{F}^*, \cdot)$. In what follows, an additive character is usually denoted by ψ, while a multiplicative one by χ. It is convenient to extend the multiplicative characters to the whole of $\mathbb{F}$, and we do so by setting $\chi(0) = 0$ for $\chi \neq 1$, respectively $\chi(0) = 1$ for $\chi = 1$.

If $\mathbb{K}$ is an extension of $\mathbb{F}$, then characters of $\mathbb{K}$ restrict to characters of $\mathbb{F}$. The other way around, characters of $\mathbb{F}$ induce characters of $\mathbb{K}$ via the trace and the norm maps: if ψ is an additive character of $\mathbb{F}$ then $\psi \circ \mathrm{Tr}$ is an additive character of $\mathbb{K}$, and if χ is a multiplicative character of $\mathbb{F}$ then $\chi \circ \mathrm{Nm}$ is a multiplicative character of $\mathbb{K}$. Note that non-trivial characters of $\mathbb{F}$ induce non-trivial characters of $\mathbb{K}$, thanks to the surjectivity of the trace and the norm.

Character sums arise by summing values of additive characters or multiplicative characters, or products thereof, over the whole field or just a subset of it. As this vague description already suggests, character sums come in a kaleidoscopic variety.

A *Gauss sum* over $\mathbb{F}$ is a character sum of the form

$$G(\psi, \chi) = \sum_{s \in \mathbb{F}^*} \psi(s)\chi(s),$$

where ψ is an additive character, and χ is a multiplicative character of $\mathbb{F}$.

Recall that Gauss's lemma concerns a sum of the above form. Specifically, the cyclotomic integer G is the Gauss sum over the field $\mathbb{Z}_p$, corresponding to the additive character $a \mapsto \zeta^a$, and the quadratic character as the multiplicative character. A general Gauss sum over a field $\mathbb{F}$ is, however, no longer a cyclotomic integer, for it combines roots of unity of order q with roots of unity of order $q - 1$. Here q is, as usual, the number of elements of $\mathbb{F}$.

The Gauss sums involving trivial characters are easily computed:

$$G(1, 1) = q - 1, \qquad G(1, \chi) = 0 \text{ for } \chi \neq 1, \qquad G(\psi, 1) = -1 \text{ for } \psi \neq 1.$$

Far more interesting is the following fact.

Theorem 6.10. If ψ and χ are non-trivial characters, then

$$\left|G(\psi, \chi)\right| = \sqrt{q}.$$

Proof. We start by expanding $\left|G(\psi, \chi)\right|^2 = G(\psi, \chi)\,\overline{G(\psi, \chi)}$:

$$\left|G(\psi, \chi)\right|^2 = \sum_{s,t \in \mathbb{F}^*} \psi(s)\overline{\psi(t)}\chi(s)\overline{\chi(t)} = \sum_{t \in \mathbb{F}^*}\sum_{s \in \mathbb{F}^*} \psi(s - t)\chi(s/t).$$

We make the change of variable $s \mapsto ts$ in the inner sum, and we continue:

$$\left|G(\psi, \chi)\right|^2 = \sum_{t \in \mathbb{F}^*}\sum_{s \in \mathbb{F}^*} \psi(t(s - 1))\chi(s) = \sum_{s \in \mathbb{F}^*} \chi(s)\sum_{t \in \mathbb{F}^*} \psi(t(s - 1)).$$

For $s = 1$ the inner sum equals $q - 1$, while for $s \neq 1$ it equals $-\psi(0) = -1$. Therefore

$$\left|G(\psi, \chi)\right|^2 = q - 1 - \sum_{1 \neq s \in \mathbb{F}^*} \chi(s) = q - \sum_{s \in \mathbb{F}^*} \chi(s) = q,$$

as claimed.   □

The previous theorem is, in effect, a generalization of Gauss's lemma. To see this, observe that

$$\overline{G(\psi, \chi)} = \sum_{s \in \mathbb{F}^*} \overline{\psi(s)}\,\overline{\chi(s)} = \sum_{s \in \mathbb{F}^*} \psi(-s)\overline{\chi}(s)$$

$$= \sum_{s \in \mathbb{F}^*} \psi(s)\overline{\chi}(-s) = \chi(-1)\sum_{s \in \mathbb{F}^*} \psi(s)\overline{\chi}(s) = \chi(-1)G(\psi, \overline{\chi}).$$

So we may restate the theorem as saying that

$$G(\psi, \chi)G(\psi, \overline{\chi}) = \chi(-1)q$$

whenever ψ and χ are non-trivial. In particular, if q is odd then we may take χ to be the quadratic character σ. As σ is real valued, we obtain $G(\psi, \sigma)^2 = \sigma(-1)q$ for any non-trivial ψ. This relation is a mild extension of Gauss's lemma.

A *Jacobi sum* over $\mathbb{F}$ is a character sum of the form

$$J(\chi_1, \chi_2) = \sum_{s+t=1} \chi_1(s)\chi_2(t),$$

where χ_1 and χ_2 are multiplicative characters.

We have already encountered a Jacobi sum in Lemma 5.4, where we found that $J(\sigma, \sigma) = -\sigma(-1)$. Note also that $J(\mathbb{1}, \mathbb{1}) = q$, and $J(\mathbb{1}, \chi) = J(\chi, \mathbb{1}) = 0$ whenever χ is non-trivial. For Jacobi sums involving non-trivial characters, their absolute values can be computed as well. This is the aim of the exercise below.

Exercise 6.11. (i) Let χ_1 and χ_2 be non-trivial multiplicative characters. Show that

$$|J(\chi_1, \chi_2)| = \begin{cases} \sqrt{q} & \text{if } \chi_1\chi_2 \neq \mathbb{1}, \\ 1 & \text{if } \chi_1\chi_2 = \mathbb{1}, \end{cases}$$

by proceeding as follows. In the first case, establish the following relation with Gauss sums: $G(\psi, \chi_1)G(\psi, \chi_2) = J(\chi_1, \chi_2)G(\psi, \chi_1\chi_2)$ for each non-trivial additive character ψ. For the second case, argue directly that $J(\chi, \chi^{-1}) = -\chi(-1)$ for any non-trivial χ.

(ii) Use the above computation, for a suitable choice of χ_1 and χ_2, to deduce Fermat's theorem: if $q \equiv 1 \bmod 4$, then q is the sum of two integral squares.

A Gauss sum is a mixed-type character sum, as it combines additive and multiplicative characters. A Jacobi sum is a convolution-type character sum. The following definition introduces yet another type: a restricted character sum.

An *Eisenstein sum* for an extension $\mathbb{K}/\mathbb{F}$ is a character sum of the form

$$E(\chi) = \sum_{\mathrm{Tr}(s)=1} \chi(s),$$

where χ is a multiplicative character of $\mathbb{K}$. One could also consider the 'singular' Eisenstein sum

$$E_0(\chi) = \sum_{\substack{\mathrm{Tr}(s)=0 \\ s \neq 0}} \chi(s),$$

but this sum plays only a secondary role, as the next lemma will show. Note at this point that, for the trivial character, we have $E(\mathbb{1}) = q^{n-1}$ and $E_0(\mathbb{1}) = q^{n-1} - 1$. As usual, n denotes the degree of the extension $\mathbb{K}/\mathbb{F}$.

Lemma 6.12. Let χ be a non-trivial character of $\mathbb{K}$. Then

$$E_0(\chi) = \begin{cases} 0 & \text{if } \chi \text{ is non-trivial on } \mathbb{F}, \\ -(q-1)E(\chi) & \text{if } \chi \text{ is trivial on } \mathbb{F}. \end{cases}$$

Proof. Decomposing over trace values, we write

$$\sum_{s \in \mathbb{K}^*} \chi(s) = E_0(\chi) + \sum_{c \in \mathbb{F}^*} \sum_{\text{Tr}(s)=c} \chi(s).$$

The left-hand sum is 0. On the right-hand side, for each $c \neq 0$ we have

$$\sum_{\text{Tr}(s)=c} \chi(s) = \chi(c)E(\chi),$$

by a change of variable $s \mapsto cs$. Thus

$$0 = E_0(\chi) + E(\chi) \sum_{c \in \mathbb{F}^*} \chi(c).$$

The latter sum is 0 or $q-1$ according to whether χ is non-trivial or trivial on $\mathbb{F}$. The claimed formulas for $E_0(\chi)$ follow.   □

The statement and the proof of the previous lemma are helpful in establishing the following fact.

Theorem 6.13. Let χ be a non-trivial character of $\mathbb{K}$. Then

$$|E(\chi)| = \begin{cases} q^{(n-1)/2} & \text{if } \chi \text{ is non-trivial on } \mathbb{F}, \\ q^{n/2-1} & \text{if } \chi \text{ is trivial on } \mathbb{F}. \end{cases}$$

Proof. Let χ_{res} denote the multiplicative character of $\mathbb{F}$ obtained by restricting χ. Also let ψ be a non-trivial additive character of $\mathbb{F}$, and denote by ψ^{ind} the additive character of $\mathbb{K}$ induced via the trace. Note that ψ^{ind} is also non-trivial.

We relate the following two Gauss sums, one over $\mathbb{K}$ and the other over $\mathbb{F}$:

$$G(\psi^{\text{ind}}, \chi) = \sum_{s \in \mathbb{K}^*} \psi(\text{Tr}(s))\chi(s), \qquad G(\psi, \chi_{\text{res}}) = \sum_{c \in \mathbb{F}^*} \psi(c)\chi(c).$$

We decompose the Gauss sum over $\mathbb{K}$ according to the values of the trace map, and we write

$$G(\psi^{\text{ind}}, \chi) = \psi(0)E_0(\chi) + \sum_{c \in \mathbb{F}^*} \psi(c)\left(\sum_{\text{Tr}(s)=c} \chi(s) \right)$$

$$= E_0(\chi) + \sum_{c \in \mathbb{F}^*} \psi(c)\chi(c)E(\chi)$$

$$= E_0(\chi) + G(\psi, \chi_{\text{res}})E(\chi).$$

Assume χ_{res} is non-trivial. Then $E_0(\chi) = 0$, and the above relation simplifies to

$$G(\psi^{\mathrm{ind}}, \chi) = G(\psi, \chi_{\mathrm{res}})E(\chi).$$

As $|G(\psi^{\mathrm{ind}}, \chi)| = q^{n/2}$, and $|G(\psi, \chi_{\mathrm{res}})| = q^{1/2}$, we get $|E(\chi)| = q^{(n-1)/2}$.

Assume χ_{res} is trivial. Then $E_0(\chi) = -(q-1)E(\chi)$ and $G(\psi, \chi_{\mathrm{res}}) = -1$. In this case, we get

$$G(\psi^{\mathrm{ind}}, \chi) = -qE(\chi).$$

Using $|G(\psi^{\mathrm{ind}}, \chi)| = q^{n/2}$ once again, we conclude that $|E(\chi)| = q^{n/2-1}$. $\qquad\square$

6.3 More character sums over finite fields

For the character sums considered so far — Gauss, Jacobi, Eisenstein sums — we have succeeded in computing their absolute values. To gain some appreciation for our computations and their relative simplicity, we need to enlarge the perspective only very slightly. Let us consider some similar-looking sums.

A *Kloosterman sum* over $\mathbb{F}$ is a character sum given by the convolution formula

$$K(\psi_1, \psi_2) = \sum_{st=1} \psi_1(s)\psi_2(t),$$

where ψ_1 and ψ_2 are additive characters. This is the counterpart of a Jacobi sum. The Kloosterman sums involving non-trivial characters can be bounded as follows.

Theorem 6.14 (Weil). If ψ_1 and ψ_2 are non-trivial, then $\left|K(\psi_1, \psi_2)\right| \leq 2\sqrt{q}$.

Now let $\mathbb{K}/\mathbb{F}$ be an extension of degree n. The restricted character sum

$$S(\psi) = \sum_{\mathrm{Nm}(s)=1} \psi(s),$$

where ψ is an additive character of $\mathbb{K}$, is the counterpart of an Eisenstein sum. Fairly simple considerations lead to the bound $|S(\psi)| \leq q^{n/2}$ for non-trivial ψ; see Exercise 6.16 below. However, when n is small with respect to q, a better bound holds.

Theorem 6.15 (Deligne). If ψ is non-trivial, then $\left|S(\psi)\right| \leq nq^{(n-1)/2}$.

Exercise 6.16. (i) Let ψ be a non-trivial additive character of $\mathbb{F}$, and d a positive integer. Show that

$$\left|\sum_{s \in \mathbb{F}} \psi(s^d)\right| \leq (d-1)\sqrt{q},$$

via the identity $\sum_{s \in \mathbb{F}^*} \psi(s^d) = \sum_{\chi^d = 1} G(\psi, \chi)$.

(ii) Let $\mathbb{K}/\mathbb{F}$ be an extension of degree n, and let ψ be a non-trivial additive character on $\mathbb{K}$. Using the above estimate, conclude that $|S(\psi)| \leq q^{n/2}$.

The previous exercise is an instance of character sums restricted to polynomial values. The following result addresses this type of character sums, in much greater generality.

Theorem 6.17 (Weil). Let $f \in \mathbb{F}[X]$ be a polynomial of degree d.

(i) Let χ be a non-trivial multiplicative character. If f is not of the form g^m, where $g \in \mathbb{F}[X]$ and m is the order of χ, then

$$\left| \sum_{s \in \mathbb{F}} \chi(f(s)) \right| \le (d-1)\sqrt{q}.$$

(ii) Let ψ be a non-trivial additive character. If d is relatively prime to q, then

$$\left| \sum_{s \in \mathbb{F}} \psi(f(s)) \right| \le (d-1)\sqrt{q}.$$

These bounds are better than the trivial bound, q, when $d \le \sqrt{q}$. The hypothesis in part (i) is clearly needed. To motivate the hypothesis in part (ii), consider the following example. Assume $q = p^e$, where $e \ge 2$. Let ψ be an additive character of $\mathbb{F}$ induced by a non-trivial character of its prime field. Also let $f = X^p - X$. Then $\psi(f(s)) = 1$ for each $s \in \mathbb{F}$. Now $\sum_{s \in \mathbb{F}} \psi(f(s)) = q$, for which $(p-1)\sqrt{q}$ is not an upper bound.

The following result is an important consequence of Theorem 6.17. Historically, it predates, and it motivated, the Weil estimates.

Corollary 6.18 (Hasse). Assume q is odd. Let N_f be the number of solutions to the equation $y^2 = f(x)$, where f is a cubic polynomial. Then $|N_f - q| \le 2\sqrt{q}$.

Proof. For each x, there are $1 + \sigma(f(x))$ solutions to $y^2 = f(x)$. Thus

$$N_f = \sum_x \left(1 + \sigma(f(x))\right) = q + \sum_x \sigma(f(x)).$$

Now

$$|N_f - q| = \left| \sum_x \sigma(f(x)) \right| \le 2\sqrt{q}$$

by applying part (i) of Theorem 6.17.   □

Note that Lemma 5.17, which we proved by elementary means, can be obtained as a consequence of the Hasse bound. If $q > 9$, then $N_f \ge q - 2\sqrt{q} > 3$, and so $N_f \ge 4$. As $y^2 = f(x)$ has at most three solutions with $y = 0$, it follows that there is at least one solution with $y \ne 0$. This means that, for $q > 9$, every cubic polynomial $f \in \mathbb{F}[X]$ has a value which is a non-zero square. Replacing f by cf, where $c \in \mathbb{F}$ is a non-square, we obtain Lemma 5.17.

Notes. Character sums over finite fields are important in algebraic and analytic number theory. We used them in the proof of quadratic reciprocity, and for counting the number of solutions for certain polynomial equations. As we will see, they also come up in the spectral study of various algebraically defined graphs.

The references for the theorems of Weil and Deligne that we have quoted are Weil (*On some exponential sums*, Proc. Nat. Acad. Sci. USA 1948; Zbl 0032.26102) and Deligne (*Cohomologie étale, SGA* $4\frac{1}{2}$, Lecture Notes in Mathematics 569, Springer 1977; Zbl 0345.00010). These are deep and difficult results, relying on ideas and techniques from algebraic geometry. Elementary approaches to Weil's theorem 6.17 are nowadays available, but they are still very involved. See Lidl and Niederreiter (*Finite fields*, Second edition, Cambridge University Press 1997; Zbl 0866.11069).

6.4 An application to Paley graphs

Let n be a positive integer. A graph is said to be *n-universal* if it contains every (possibly disconnected) graph on n vertices as an induced subgraph. The key requirement here is that subgraphs should be induced — meaning that they inherit all edges of the ambient graph.

Evidently, n-universal graphs exist. It is less evident that n-universal graphs exist among highly regular graphs, such as strongly regular graphs or Cayley graphs.

Theorem 6.19. Let n be a positive integer. Then, for q large enough with respect to n, the Paley graph $P(q)$ is n-universal.

Proof. A simple-minded strategy for realizing a graph on n vertices inside $P(q)$ is to do it vertex by vertex. For this to succeed, we need to show that $P(q)$ enjoys the following property for q large enough: given a set of vertices A with $|A| = k \in \{1, \ldots, n-1\}$, and a partition of A into two subsets C ('connect') and D ('disconnect'), there is a 'new' vertex $v \notin A$ such that v is connected to each vertex in C but to no vertex in D.

The desired vertex $v \notin A$ has to satisfy $\sigma(v-c) = 1$ for all $c \in C$, and $\sigma(v-d) \neq 1$ for all $d \in D$. In other words, we need $\tau(v) \neq 0$, where

$$\tau(v) = \prod_{c \in C} \left(1 + \sigma(v - c)\right) \prod_{d \in D} \left(1 - \sigma(v - d)\right).$$

We will show that such a vertex exists by showing that $\sum_{v \notin A} \tau(v) > 0$ for q large enough. To that end, we need an upper bound for $\sum_{v \in A} \tau(v)$, and a lower bound for $\sum_{v \in \mathbb{F}} \tau(v)$.

When $v \in A$, $\tau(v)$ is either 0 or 2^{k-1}. As $k = |A|$ is small in comparison to $q = |\mathbb{F}|$, we can afford the following bound:

$$\sum_{v \in A} \tau(v) \leq k2^{k-1}. \tag{6.1}$$

On the other hand, expanding the product that defines $\tau(v)$, we get

$$\tau(v) = 1 + \sum_{\emptyset \neq S \subseteq A} (-1)^{|S \cap D|} \sigma(f_S(v)), \quad f_S(v) := \prod_{s \in S}(v - s),$$

so

$$\sum_{v \in \mathbb{F}} \tau(v) = q + \sum_{\emptyset \neq S \subseteq A} (-1)^{|S \cap D|} \sum_{v \in \mathbb{F}} \sigma(f_S(v)).$$

At this point, we employ the Weil character bound:

$$\left| \sum_{v \in \mathbb{F}} \sigma(f_S(v)) \right| \leq (|S| - 1)\sqrt{q}.$$

We obtain

$$\sum_{v \in \mathbb{F}} \tau(v) \geq q - \sum_{\emptyset \neq S \subseteq A} (|S| - 1)\sqrt{q} = q - \sqrt{q} \sum_{i=1}^{k}(i-1)\binom{k}{i}$$

and

$$\sum_{i=1}^{k}(i-1)\binom{k}{i} = k\sum_{i=1}^{k}\binom{k-1}{i-1} - \sum_{i=1}^{k}\binom{k}{i} = k2^{k-1} - (2^k - 1) \leq k2^{k-1} - 1.$$

Thus

$$\sum_{v \in \mathbb{F}} \tau(v) \geq q - (k2^{k-1} - 1)\sqrt{q}. \tag{6.2}$$

Now (6.1) and (6.2) imply that $\sum_{v \notin A} \tau(v) > 0$ whenever $q - (k2^{k-1} - 1)\sqrt{q} > k2^{k-1}$, that is, $\sqrt{q} > k2^{k-1}$. This holds for each $k \in \{1, \ldots, n-1\}$ when $\sqrt{q} > (n-1)2^{n-2}$. □

Notes. The interest in n-universal graphs starts with Moon (*On minimal n-universal graphs*, Proc. Glasgow Math. Assoc. 1965; Zbl 0132.21202). He showed that an n-universal graph has at least $2^{(n-1)/2}$ vertices.

Theorem 6.19 is due to Bollobás and Thomason (*Graphs which contain all small graphs*, European J. Combin. 1981; Zbl 0471.05037), and to Blass, Exoo, and Harary (*Paley graphs satisfy all first-order adjacency axioms*, J. Graph Theory 1981; Zbl 0472.05058). It is a slight variation of the following earlier result of Graham and Spencer (*A constructive solution to a tournament problem*, Canad. Math. Bull.

1971; Zbl 0209.55804). Let $\mathbb{F}$ be a finite field with q elements, where $q \equiv 3 \bmod 4$. Thus, -1 is not a square in $\mathbb{F}$. Now consider the complete graph on the elements of $\mathbb{F}$, and orient each edge by the rule that $x \to y$ if and only if $x - y$ is a square. Such a directed complete graph can be thought of as a tournament in which every player meets every other player, and no game ends in a draw. The Graham–Spencer result is that the 'Paley tournament' we have just described enjoys the following paradoxical property: for q large enough with respect to a given n, every set of n players is beaten by some other player. This is an organizers' nightmare, for who gets to win such a tournament?

7

Eigenvalues of graphs

This chapter opens the second part of this text, devoted to the spectral perspective on graphs. The first part serves as a long motivation.

7.1 Adjacency and Laplacian eigenvalues

The two most important matrices associated to a graph are the adjacency matrix and the Laplacian matrix. Both are square matrices indexed by the vertex set V. The *adjacency matrix A* is given by

$$A(u, v) = \begin{cases} 1 & \text{if } u \sim v, \\ 0 & \text{otherwise,} \end{cases}$$

while the *Laplacian matrix L* is defined as

$$L(u, v) = \begin{cases} \deg(v) & \text{if } u = v, \\ -1 & \text{if } u \sim v, \\ 0 & \text{otherwise.} \end{cases}$$

The two matrices are related by the formula

$$A + L = \text{diag(deg)},$$

where diag(deg) denotes the diagonal matrix recording the degrees.

We often view the adjacency matrix and the Laplacian matrix as operators on $\ell^2 V$. Recall that $\ell^2 V$ is the finite-dimensional space of complex-valued functions on V, endowed with the inner product

$$\langle f, g \rangle = \sum_v f(v)\overline{g(v)}.$$

The adjacency operator $A : \ell^2 V \to \ell^2 V$ and the Laplacian operator $L : \ell^2 V \to \ell^2 V$ are given by

$$Af(v) = \sum_{u:u \sim v} f(u),$$

respectively

$$Lf(v) = \deg(v)f(v) - \sum_{u:u\sim v} f(u).$$

We have the following useful formulas:

$$\langle Af, f \rangle = \sum_{u\sim v} f(u)\overline{f(v)} = \sum_{\{u,v\}\in E} 2\,\mathrm{Re}\left(f(u)\overline{f(v)}\right), \tag{7.1}$$

$$\langle Lf, f \rangle = \frac{1}{2}\sum_{u\sim v} |f(u) - f(v)|^2 = \sum_{\{u,v\}\in E} |f(u) - f(v)|^2. \tag{7.2}$$

Note the distinction between summing over adjacencies and summing over edges. Formula (7.1) is immediate from the definition of A, and (7.2) can be deduced from (7.1). Formula (7.2) is particularly appealing: the right-most sum can be interpreted as an overall edge differential.

The adjacency matrix A and the Laplacian matrix L are real symmetric matrices. (Strictly speaking, viewing them as actual matrices involves a numbering of the vertices. Different numberings yield different, but conjugate matrices.) Recall, at this point, the spectral theorem: if M is a real, symmetric $n \times n$ matrix, then there is an orthogonal basis consisting of eigenvectors, and M has n real eigenvalues, counted with multiplicities. Thus, both A and L have $n = |V|$ real eigenvalues. In fact, the eigenvalues are algebraic integers (roots of monic polynomials with integral coefficients) since both A and L have integral entries.

Our convention is that the adjacency, respectively the Laplacian, eigenvalues, are denoted and ordered as

$$\alpha_{\min} = \alpha_n \leq \cdots \leq \alpha_2 \leq \alpha_1 = \alpha_{\max},$$
$$\lambda_{\min} = \lambda_1 \leq \lambda_2 \leq \cdots \leq \lambda_n = \lambda_{\max}.$$

Here n denotes, as usual, the number of vertices. For the purposes of relating eigenvalues to graph invariants, the most important eigenvalues will turn out to be the extremal ones, as well as λ_2 and α_2.

The *spectrum* is the multiset of eigenvalues, that is, the set of eigenvalues repeated according to their multiplicity. Occasionally, we write α-spec for the adjacency spectrum, respectively λ-spec for the Laplacian spectrum.

For regular graphs, the Laplacian matrix and the adjacency matrix carry the same spectral information. Indeed, $A + L = dI$, so $\alpha_k + \lambda_k = d$ and the corresponding eigenvectors are the same. Thus, using the Laplacian or the adjacency spectrum is mostly a matter of convenience in the regular case. Even for non-regular graphs, there is a kind of silent duality between adjacency and Laplacian eigenvalues.

A guiding principle of spectral graph theory is that much knowledge about a graph can be extracted from spectral information. But could it be that spectral information gives complete knowledge about a graph? The answer is a resounding no. As we will see, there are many examples of *isospectral* but non-isomorphic regular graphs. As one might guess, two regular graphs are said to be isospectral when they have the same adjacency (equivalently, Laplacian) spectrum. Note that we consider isospectrality only in the context of regular graphs. Of course, the same issue can be pursued for non-regular graphs, but then there are two distinct sides to the story.

Notes. Perhaps the most conceptual way of motivating the combinatorial Laplacian is the following. Choose an orientation on the edges, and define the operator D : $\ell^2 V \to \ell^2 E$ as $Df(e) = f(e^+) - f(e^-)$, where e^+ and e^- denote the terminal and the initial vertices, respectively, of the edge e. We think of D as a discrete differential operator. Then $L = D^*D$, where D^* is the adjoint of D. An analogous formula defines the geometric Laplacian Δ on manifolds, with the gradient operator in place of D. This analogy explains the name attached to L, as well as the other common notation for the graph-theoretic Laplacian, Δ.

The Laplacian of a graph can be traced back to work of Kirchhoff from 1847 on electrical networks. Not only the time, but also the result is surprising: in a modern formulation, Kirchhoff's matrix-tree theorem gives a formula for the number of spanning trees in a graph in terms of its Laplacian eigenvalues. Interest in the Laplacian eigenvalues was revived in the early 1970s by the works of Fiedler (*Algebraic connectivity of graphs*, Czechoslovak Math. J. 1973; Zbl 0265.05119) and Anderson and Morley (*Eigenvalues of the Laplacian of a graph*, Preprint 1971, Linear and Multilinear Algebra 1985; Zbl 0594.05046).

7.2 First properties

There are similarities between the adjacency approach and the Laplacian approach to the spectra of graphs. But sometimes one viewpoint sees what the other does not. One crucial point in favour of the Laplacian is the following observation.

Theorem 7.1. 0 is a Laplacian eigenvalue, having the constant function $\mathbb{1}$ as an eigenfunction. Furthermore, 0 is a simple eigenvalue.

Proof. The first part is easily checked:

$$L\mathbb{1}(v) = \deg(v) - \sum_{u:u\sim v} 1 = 0$$

for each vertex v. Now let us prove that 0 is a simple Laplacian eigenvalue. If f is an associated eigenfunction, then $Lf = 0$ and so

$$0 = \langle Lf, f \rangle = \sum_{\{u,v\}\in E} |f(u) - f(v)|^2$$

in view of (7.2). This means that $f(u) = f(v)$ whenever u is adjacent to v, and so f must be constant.   □

This theorem prompts us to refer to 0 as the trivial Laplacian eigenvalue. In the proof, we have implicitly used the assumption that graphs are connected. In general, the proof shows that the multiplicity of 0 as a Laplacian eigenvalue is the number of connected components of a graph. So the connectivity of a graph can be read off from the Laplacian spectrum. On the other hand, one cannot see the connectivity of a graph from its adjacency spectrum. See Example 7.15 for a simple illustration.

Corollary 7.2. For a regular graph, the degree d is a simple eigenvalue, with the constant function $\mathbb{1}$ as an eigenfunction.

Note that, conversely, if $\mathbb{1}$ is an adjacency eigenfunction then the graph is regular. For a regular graph, the degree is the trivial adjacency eigenvalue.

The adjacency spectrum of a graph has a combinatorial content that is manifested by the formula

$$\sum_k \alpha_k^r = \operatorname{Tr} A^r, \quad r = 1, 2, \dots. \tag{7.3}$$

The point of this formula is that the right-hand side counts the closed paths of length r in the graph. Indeed, the (u, v)-entry of A^r equals the number of paths of length r joining the two vertices u and v. For $r = 1$ and $r = 2$ we have

$$\sum_k \alpha_k = \operatorname{Tr} A = 0,$$
$$\sum_k \alpha_k^2 = \operatorname{Tr} A^2 = \sum \deg(v) = 2|E|.$$

Among other things, formula (7.3) is relevant for the following important fact.

Theorem 7.3. A graph is bipartite if and only if its adjacency spectrum is symmetric about 0.

Proof. Consider a bipartite graph. Let α be an adjacency eigenvalue, and let f be a corresponding eigenfunction. Define a new function by switching the sign of f on one side of the graph: $g = f$ on $V_\bullet$ and $g = -f$ on $V_\circ$. Then $Ag = -\alpha g$, so $-\alpha$ is an adjacency eigenvalue as well.

Conversely, assume that the adjacency spectrum of a graph is symmetric about 0. Then, for each odd $r \geq 1$, we have $\operatorname{Tr} A^r = \sum_k \alpha_k^r = 0$. This means that there are no closed paths of odd length, so the given graph is bipartite.   □

Combining the previous theorem with Corollary 7.2, we deduce the following: a d-regular bipartite graph has d and $-d$ as simple adjacency eigenvalues. In this case, $\pm d$ are deemed to be the trivial adjacency eigenvalues.

Exercise 7.4. Show that the regularity of a graph can be read off from its Laplacian spectrum.

One of our main concerns is understanding the spectral distribution of a graph. The size of a graph counts the number of eigenvalues with multiplicity. The maximal degree, on the other hand, is the main quantifier for their location. We will see several manifestations of this idea, the most basic being the following:

Theorem 7.5. The adjacency eigenvalues lie in the interval $[-d, d]$. The Laplacian eigenvalues lie in the interval $[0, 2d]$.

In particular, $\lambda_{\min} = 0$ in light of Theorem 7.1.

Proof. Let α be an adjacency eigenvalue, with eigenfunction f. Consider the eigen-relation

$$\alpha f(v) = \sum_{u:u\sim v} f(u)$$

at a vertex v where $|f|$ achieves its maximum. Then $|\alpha| |f(v)| \leq \deg(v)|f(v)| \leq d|f(v)|$, so $|\alpha| \leq d$.

Similarly, let λ be a Laplacian eigenvalue, with eigenfunction g. Arguing as before, we use the eigenrelation

$$(\deg(v) - \lambda)g(v) = \sum_{u:u\sim v} g(u)$$

at a vertex v where $|g|$ achieves its maximum. We obtain $|\deg(v) - \lambda| \leq \deg(v)$, hence $0 \leq \lambda \leq 2\deg(v) \leq 2d$.

Let us give an alternate argument. We claim that $0 \leq \langle Lf, f \rangle \leq 2d\langle f, f \rangle$ for every $f \in \ell^2 V$. The key fact is (7.2) — it obviously gives the lower bound, but also the upper bound:

$$\langle Lf, f \rangle = \frac{1}{2} \sum_{u\sim v} |f(u) - f(v)|^2 \leq \sum_{u\sim v} (|f(u)|^2 + |f(v)|^2) = 2 \sum_v \deg(v)|f(v)|^2$$

$$\leq 2d \sum_v |f(v)|^2 = 2d\langle f, f \rangle.$$

Now let λ be a Laplacian eigenvalue, with eigenfunction g. Then $\langle Lg, g \rangle = \lambda\langle g, g \rangle$, and $0 \leq \lambda \leq 2d$ follows from the above claim.   □

As we know, if a graph is regular and bipartite then $2d$ is achieved as a Laplacian eigenvalue. The converse also holds, and we see this thanks to the previous alternate argument. Indeed, let $2d$ be a Laplacian eigenvalue. Then an affiliated eigenfunction g satisfies $\langle Lg, g \rangle = 2d\langle g, g \rangle$. This means that, in the estimate displayed above, both inequalities are in fact equalities. The first is an equality when $g(u) + g(v) = 0$ for every pair of adjacent vertices u and v. By connectivity, there is a constant $c \neq 0$ such that g is $\pm c$-valued. The choice of sign corresponds to a bipartite structure on the graph. As g never vanishes, the second inequality is an equality when every vertex has degree d. In conclusion, the graph is regular and bipartite.

The number of *distinct* eigenvalues can be nicely and usefully related to the diameter. This is a first illustration of another one of our main themes, that of relating adjacency and Laplacian eigenvalues with graph-theoretical invariants.

Theorem 7.6. The number of distinct adjacency, respectively Laplacian, eigenvalues is greater than the diameter.

Proof. Let u and v be two distinct vertices. Then $A^r(u, v) = 0$ for $r = 0, \ldots,$ $\text{dist}(u, v) - 1$, while $A^r(u, v) \neq 0$ for $r = \text{dist}(u, v)$. Note that the same is true for L. On the other hand, a symmetric matrix M with exactly s distinct eigenvalues satisfies a monic polynomial relation of degree s. Thus, M^s is a linear combination of $\{M^r : r = 0, \ldots, s - 1\}$, and this continues to hold for higher powers M^r, $r \geq s$. We deduce that the number of distinct eigenvalues — adjacency or Laplacian — is greater than $\text{dist}(u, v)$ for any two vertices u and v, hence greater than the diameter. $\square$

It is certainly possible for a graph to have more than diam $+1$ distinct eigenvalues. Two families of graphs of diameter 2 but arbitrarily many distinct eigenvalues are the wheel graphs and the Andrásfai graphs; these are discussed in ensuing exercises. Nevertheless, most graphs considered herein turn out to have exactly diam $+1$ distinct eigenvalues. There are worse habits than mentally checking, whenever faced with a concrete list of eigenvalues for a graph, whether this diameter bound is attained or not.

7.3 First examples

In addition to the general theory, we wish to build a stock of concrete spectral computations. We start with some basic examples, including K_n, C_n, Q_n.

Example 7.7. The complete graph K_n has adjacency matrix $A = J - I$, where J is the matrix all of whose entries are 1. The matrix J has eigenvalues 0, with multiplicity $n - 1$, and n. So the adjacency eigenvalues are -1, with multiplicity $n - 1$, and $n - 1$. The Laplacian eigenvalues are 0, respectively n with multiplicity $n - 1$.

Example 7.8. Consider the cycle graph C_n, and label its vertices $1, \ldots, n$ in a circular fashion. Let α be an adjacency eigenvalue, with eigenfunction f. Then the following relations hold: generically, $\alpha f_k = f_{k-1} + f_{k+1}$ for $k = 1, \ldots, n - 1$; exceptionally, $\alpha f_1 = f_2 + f_n$, , and $\alpha f_n = f_{n-1} + f_1$.

The generic relations describe a quadratic recurrence whose solution is $f_k = ax_1^k + bx_2^k$, where x_1 and x_2 are the roots of $x^2 - \alpha x + 1 = 0$. The exceptional relations read as initial and terminal conditions: $f_0 = f_n$, $f_1 = f_{n+1}$. This means that the two relations $a + b = ax_1^n + bx_2^n$ and $ax_1 + bx_2 = ax_1^{n+1} + bx_2^{n+1}$ admit a non-zero solution (a, b). Keeping in mind that $x_1 x_2 = 1$, simple arguments lead to $x_1^n = x_2^n = 1$. Put $x_1 = \xi$, $x_2 = \bar{\xi}$, where $\xi^n = 1$. Then $\alpha = x_1 + x_2 = 2\operatorname{Re}(\xi)$, and $f_k = a\xi^k + b\bar{\xi}^k$ for $k = 0, \ldots, n$.

In conclusion, the adjacency eigenvalues of C_n are $2\cos(2\pi k/n)$ for $k = 0, \ldots, n-1$.

Rule 7.9. Consider the product $X \times Y$ of two graphs X and Y. Given two maps $f : V(X) \to \mathbb{C}$ and $g : V(Y) \to \mathbb{C}$, let $f \times g : V(X \times Y) \to \mathbb{C}$ denote the map given by $(x, y) \mapsto f(x)g(y)$. On such functions, the adjacency and the Laplacian operators for $X \times Y$ can be expressed as

$$A(f \times g) = A_X(f) \times g + f \times A_Y(g),$$
$$L(f \times g) = L_X(f) \times g + f \times L_Y(g).$$

The verification is left to the reader. Consequently, if f is an eigenfunction on X and g is an eigenfunction on Y, then $f \times g$ is an eigenfunction on $X \times Y$, with eigenvalue equal to the sum of the eigenvalues for f and g. There are no further eigenvalues for $X \times Y$ besides the ones obtained in this way. Indeed, note that $\langle f \times g, f' \times g' \rangle = \langle f, f' \rangle \langle g, g' \rangle$. So, if $\{f_i\}_i$ and $\{g_j\}_j$ are orthogonal bases of eigenfunctions on X, respectively Y, then $\{f_i \times g_j\}_{i,j}$ is an orthogonal basis of eigenfunctions on $X \times Y$. We conclude that the eigenvalues of the product $X \times Y$ are obtained by adding the eigenvalues of X to those of Y:

$$\alpha\text{-spec}(X \times Y) = \alpha\text{-spec}(X) + \alpha\text{-spec}(Y),$$
$$\lambda\text{-spec}(X \times Y) = \lambda\text{-spec}(X) + \lambda\text{-spec}(Y).$$

Example 7.10. Consider the cube graph Q_n, thought of as the n-fold product of $K_2 \times \cdots \times K_2$. The graph K_2 has two simple eigenvalues, 1 and -1. Hence the adjacency eigenvalues of Q_n are $(n - k) \cdot 1 + k \cdot (-1) = n - 2k$ with multiplicity $\binom{n}{k}$, for $k = 0, \ldots, n$.

Rule 7.11. For a disconnected graph, the adjacency and the Laplacian operators admit a natural block-diagonal form, with a block for each connected component. So the eigenvalues of a disconnected graph are obtained by piling together the eigenvalues of its connected components:

$$\alpha\text{-spec}(X \sqcup Y) = \alpha\text{-spec}(X) \cup \alpha\text{-spec}(Y),$$
$$\lambda\text{-spec}(X \sqcup Y) = \lambda\text{-spec}(X) \cup \lambda\text{-spec}(Y).$$

Exercise 7.12. The *complement* of a (possibly disconnected) graph X has the same vertex set as X, and two distinct vertices are adjacent whenever they are not adjacent in X.

  (i) Compute the Laplacian spectrum of the complement of X in terms of the Laplacian spectrum of X.
  (ii) Find the Laplacian spectrum of the complete k-partite graph $K_{n_1,...,n_k}$. This is the graph defined as follows: the vertex set is the disjoint union of $k \geq 2$ non-empty sets of size $n_1, \ldots, n_k$, with edges connecting vertices lying in different sets.

Exercise 7.13. The *cone* over a (possibly disconnected) graph X is the graph obtained by adding a new vertex, and joining it to all vertices of X.

  (i) Describe the Laplacian spectrum of the cone over X in terms of the Laplacian spectrum of X.
  (ii) Do the same for the adjacency spectrum, assuming that X is regular.
  (iii) Find the adjacency and Laplacian spectra of a star graph and a windmill graph. Compare the diameter and the number of distinct eigenvalues for a wheel graph with a large enough number of spokes.

Rule 7.14. Let X be a non-bipartite graph, and consider its bipartite double X'. Then the adjacency matrix of X' has the form

$$A' = \begin{pmatrix} 0 & A \\ A & 0 \end{pmatrix},$$

where A is the adjacency matrix of X. Therefore

$$A'^2 = \begin{pmatrix} A^2 & 0 \\ 0 & A^2 \end{pmatrix}.$$

Keeping in mind that the spectrum of A' is symmetric, it follows that the eigenvalues of A' are $\pm\alpha$ with α running over the eigenvalues of A. In short, the adjacency spectrum of a bipartite double is the symmetrized adjacency spectrum of the original graph:

$$\alpha\text{-spec}(X') = \pm\alpha\text{-spec}(X).$$

Example 7.15. Consider the complete bipartite graph $K_{m,n}$. Squaring the adjacency matrix A of $K_{m,n}$ yields

$$A^2 = \begin{pmatrix} C_\bullet & 0 \\ 0 & C_\circ \end{pmatrix}, \quad C_\bullet = nJ_m, \quad C_\circ = mJ_n.$$

The eigenvalues of $C_\bullet = nJ_m$ are mn with multiplicity 1, and 0 with multiplicity $m - 1$. Interchanging m and n, $C_\circ = mJ_n$ has eigenvalues mn with multiplicity 1, and

0 with multiplicity $n - 1$. So the eigenvalues of A are $\pm\sqrt{mn}$, each with multiplicity 1, and 0 with multiplicity $m + n - 2$.

For instance, the adjacency eigenvalues of $K_{1,4}$ are 0 with multiplicity 3, and the simple eigenvalues ± 2; the adjacency eigenvalues of $K_{2,2}$ are 0 with multiplicity 2, and the simple eigenvalues ± 2. Therefore, $K_{1,4}$ (a connected graph) and the union of $K_{2,2}$ with a singleton (a disconnected graph) have the same adjacency spectrum.

8

Eigenvalue computations

We have already computed the eigenvalues of some graphs. The focus of this chapter is on methods that are more or less explicit, and that apply to certain classes of regular graphs. We restrict our attention to their adjacency eigenvalues.

8.1 Cayley graphs and bi-Cayley graphs of abelian groups

Due to their algebraic origin, Cayley graphs can be quite tractable when it comes to understanding their spectral properties. The most basic result in this direction addresses the case of abelian groups.

Theorem 8.1. Consider the Cayley graph of a finite abelian group G with respect to S, a symmetric generating subset not containing the identity. Then the adjacency eigenvalues are $\{\alpha_\chi : \chi \in G^\wedge\}$, where

$$\alpha_\chi = \sum_{s \in S} \chi(s). \tag{8.1}$$

Proof. Let χ be a character of G. Then, for each $g \in G$, we have

$$A\chi(g) = \sum_{h:h \sim g} \chi(h) = \sum_{s \in S} \chi(gs) = \left(\sum_{s \in S} \chi(s)\right)\chi(g) = \alpha_\chi \chi(g).$$

So χ is an adjacency eigenfunction with eigenvalue α_χ. As the characters form a basis of $\ell^2 G$, there cannot be any further eigenvalues. □

The notation (8.1) will be much used in what follows. To begin, let us note that the trivial character yields the trivial adjacency eigenvalue: $\alpha_{\mathbb{1}} = |S|$.

Example 8.2. Consider the cycle graph C_n, and let us view it as the Cayley graph of the cyclic group $\mathbb{Z}_n$ with respect to $\{\pm 1\}$. The characters of $\mathbb{Z}_n$ are $\chi_k, k = 0, \ldots, n-1$, where χ_k is defined by $\chi_k(1) = \cos(2\pi k/n) + i \sin(2\pi k/n)$. So the adjacency eigenvalues of C_n are $\alpha_{(k)} = \chi_k(1) + \chi_k(-1) = 2\cos(2\pi k/n)$ for $k = 0, \ldots, n-1$.

Example 8.3. Consider the cube graph Q_n. We view it as the Cayley graph of $(\mathbb{Z}_2)^n$ with respect to $\{e_i : 1 \leq i \leq n\}$. The characters of $(\mathbb{Z}_2)^n$ are $\chi_I(v) = (-1)^{\Sigma_{i \in I} v_i}$ for $I \subseteq \{1, \ldots, n\}$. The adjacency eigenvalue corresponding to χ_I is

$$\alpha_I = \sum_{j=1}^{n} \chi_I(e_j) = \sum_{j \in I}(-1) + \sum_{j \notin I}(1) = n - 2|I|.$$

So the adjacency eigenvalues of Q_n are $\{n - 2k : k = 0, \ldots, n\}$.

Example 8.4. Consider the Paley graph $P(q)$, where $q \equiv 1 \bmod 4$. The trivial adjacency eigenvalue is $\frac{1}{2}(q - 1)$. The non-trivial eigenvalues are given by the character sums

$$\alpha_\psi = \sum_{s \in (\mathbb{F}^*)^2} \psi(s)$$

as ψ runs over the non-trivial additive characters of $\mathbb{F}$. Let us write α_ψ in terms of the Gauss sum $G(\psi, \sigma)$, where σ is the quadratic character. By adding the notation $\sum_{s \in \mathbb{F}^*} \psi(s)\sigma(s) = G(\psi, \sigma)$ to the relation $\sum_{s \in \mathbb{F}^*} \psi(s) = -1$, we find that

$$\alpha_\psi = \frac{1}{2}(G(\psi, \sigma) - 1).$$

Recall, from the discussion following Theorem 6.10, that $G(\psi, \sigma)^2 = \sigma(-1)q$. Here $\sigma(-1) = 1$, as $q \equiv 1 \bmod 4$, so $G(\psi, \sigma) = \pm\sqrt{q}$. But we also have

$$\sum_{\psi \neq 1} G(\psi, \sigma) = \sum_{s \in \mathbb{F}^*} \sigma(s) \sum_{\psi \neq 1} \psi(s) = -\sum_{s \in \mathbb{F}^*} \sigma(s) = 0,$$

meaning that the sign of $G(\psi, \sigma)$ is equally often positive as it is negative. We conclude that the non-trivial adjacency eigenvalues of $P(q)$ are $\frac{1}{2}(\pm\sqrt{q} - 1)$, and they both have multiplicity $\frac{1}{2}(q - 1)$.

Exercise 8.5. Find the Laplacian eigenvalues of the halved cube graph $\frac{1}{2}Q_n$, by using Theorem 8.1.

Exercise 8.6. Find the adjacency spectrum of the Andrasfái graph A_n. Compare the diameter and the number of distinct eigenvalues.

Exercise 8.7. Let $\mathbb{F}$ be a finite field with q elements. Consider the additive group $\mathbb{F}^n$, where $n \geq 2$.

(i) Let χ be a non-trivial additive character of $\mathbb{F}$. For $a \in \mathbb{F}^n$, let $\chi_a : \mathbb{F}^n \to \mathbb{C}$ be given by $\chi_a(x_1, \ldots, x_n) = \chi(a_1 x_1 + \cdots + a_n x_n)$. Check that each χ_a is a character of $\mathbb{F}^n$, and that $a \mapsto \chi_a$ defines an isomorphism between $\mathbb{F}^n$ and its dual.

(ii) Consider the Cayley graph of $\mathbb{F}^n$ with respect to the symmetric set $\{(s, st, \ldots, st^{n-1}) : s, t \in \mathbb{F}^*\}$. Clearly, the largest adjacency eigenvalue is $(q-1)^2$. What is the second largest, respectively the smallest eigenvalue? For which values of n is S a generating subset?

We now turn to bi-Cayley graphs of abelian groups. The following is an adaptation of Theorem 8.1 to this setting, and we continue using the notation (8.1).

Theorem 8.8. Consider the bi-Cayley graph of a finite abelian G with respect to S. Then the adjacency eigenvalues are $\{\pm|\alpha_\chi| : \chi \in G^\wedge\}$.

Proof. Let χ be a character of G. We look for an adjacency eigenfunction θ of the form $\theta = \chi$ on $G_\bullet$, and $\theta = c(\chi)\chi$ on $G_\circ$ for a suitable non-zero scalar $c(\chi)$. A good choice is

$$c(\chi) = \frac{\overline{\alpha_\chi}}{|\alpha_\chi|},$$

with the convention that $c(\chi) = 1$ when $\alpha_\chi = 0$. Indeed, we have

$$A\theta(g_\bullet) = \sum_{h_\circ \sim g_\bullet} \theta(h_\circ) = c(\chi) \sum_{s \in S} \chi(gs) = c(\chi)\alpha_\chi\chi(g) = |\alpha_\chi|\theta(g_\bullet),$$

$$A\theta(g_\circ) = \sum_{h_\bullet \sim g_\circ} \theta(h_\bullet) = \sum_{s \in S} \chi(gs^{-1}) = \overline{\alpha_\chi}\chi(g) = |\alpha_\chi|\theta(g_\circ),$$

and so θ is an eigenfunction with eigenvalue $|\alpha_\chi|$. Switching the sign of θ on $G_\circ$ produces an eigenfunction θ' with eigenvalue $-|\alpha_\chi|$. The $2|G|$ eigenfunctions we have found, $\theta = \theta(\chi)$ and $\theta' = \theta'(\chi)$ for χ running over the characters of G, are easily seen to be linearly independent. So there are no further eigenvalues.   □

For Cayley graphs of abelian groups, the characters provide a basis of eigenfunctions that does not depend on the choice of S. Here, characters provide a basis of eigenfunctions that does depend on S, but in a rather weak way: namely, the phase $c(\chi)$ depends on S.

Example 8.9. Consider the bi-Paley graph $BP(q)$, for $q \equiv 3 \bmod 4$. If again we put

$$\alpha_\psi = \sum_{s \in (\mathbb{F}^*)^2} \psi(s),$$

then the non-trivial eigenvalues of $BP(q)$ are $\pm|\alpha_\psi|$ as ψ runs over the non-trivial additive characters of $\mathbb{F}$. We still have $\alpha_\psi = \frac{1}{2}(G(\psi, \sigma) - 1)$, but now $G(\psi, \sigma)^2 = \sigma(-1)q = -q$. Thus $\alpha_\psi = \frac{1}{2}(-1 \pm i\sqrt{q})$, and so $|\alpha_\psi| = \frac{1}{2}\sqrt{q+1}$. In conclusion, the adjacency eigenvalues of $BP(q)$ are $\pm\frac{1}{2}(q-1)$ and $\pm\frac{1}{2}\sqrt{q+1}$.

Example 8.10. The incidence graph $I_n(q)$ may be viewed as the bi-Cayley graph of the multiplicative group $\mathbb{K}^*/\mathbb{F}^*$ with respect to the subset $\{[s] : \mathrm{Tr}(s) = 0\}$. Here $\mathbb{K}$ is a degree-n extension of $\mathbb{F}$, and $\mathrm{Tr} : \mathbb{K} \to \mathbb{F}$ is the trace. The characters of $\mathbb{K}^*/\mathbb{F}^*$ correspond, through the quotient homomorphism $[\cdot] : \mathbb{K}^* \to \mathbb{K}^*/\mathbb{F}^*$, to the multiplicative characters of $\mathbb{K}$ that are trivial on $\mathbb{F}$. So the adjacency eigenvalues are $\pm|\alpha_{[\chi]}|$, where

$$\alpha_{[\chi]} = \sum_{\substack{[s]\in\mathbb{K}^*/\mathbb{F}^* \\ \mathrm{Tr}(s)=0}} [\chi]([s]) = \frac{1}{q-1} \sum_{\substack{s\in\mathbb{K}^* \\ \mathrm{Tr}(s)=0}} \chi(s) = \frac{1}{q-1}E_0(\chi).$$

Recall, $E_0(\chi)$ denotes the singular Eisenstein sum associated to χ. The trivial character yields the simple eigenvalues $\pm|\alpha_{[1]}| = \pm(q^{n-1} - 1)/(q - 1)$. For a non-trivial χ, we have $E_0(\chi) = -(q - 1)E(\chi)$ by Lemma 6.12, and so

$$\alpha_{[\chi]} = -E(\chi).$$

Applying Theorem 6.13, we obtain the eigenvalues $\pm|\alpha_{[\chi]}| = \pm q^{n/2-1}$, each with multiplicity $|\mathbb{K}^*/\mathbb{F}^*| - 1 = (q^n - q)/(q - 1)$.

Notes. For a Cayley graph coming from an abelian group, the eigenvalues are given by character sums. It turns out that the same holds when general groups are involved. This requires, however, a general theory of characters which is outside the scope of this text. See Babai (*Spectra of Cayley graphs*, J. Combin. Theory Ser. B 1979; Zbl 0338.05110) and also the discussion of Murty (*Ramanujan graphs*, J. Ramanujan Math. Soc. 2003; Zbl 1038.05038).

8.2 Strongly regular graphs

Recall that a strongly regular graph is a regular graph with the property that, for some non-negative integers a and c, any two adjacent vertices have a common neighbours, and any two distinct non-adjacent vertices have c common neighbours.

   A strongly regular graph has diameter 2, so we expect at least three distinct eigenvalues. The following proposition explicitly computes the adjacency eigenvalues, and their multiplicities, for a strongly regular graph.

Theorem 8.11. A strongly regular graph has three distinct adjacency eigenvalues. In terms of the parameters (n, d, a, c), they are given as follows: the simple eigenvalue d, and two more eigenvalues

$$\frac{a - c \pm \sqrt{\mathrm{disc}}}{2}, \quad \mathrm{disc} = (a - c)^2 + 4(d - c) > 0,$$

with corresponding multiplicities

$$\frac{1}{2}\left(n - 1 \mp \frac{(n-1)(a-c) + 2d}{\sqrt{\text{disc}}}\right).$$

Conversely, a regular graph having three distinct adjacency eigenvalues is strongly regular.

Proof. Squaring the adjacency matrix A, we see that $A^2(u, v)$ equals d if $u = v$, a if $u \sim v$, and c otherwise. Therefore $A^2 = (a - c)A + (d - c)I + cJ$, where J is the $n \times n$ matrix all of whose entries are 1.

Now let α be a non-trivial eigenvalue, with eigenfunction f. Applying the above relation to f, and keeping in mind that $Jf = 0$, we get $\alpha^2 = (a - c)\alpha + (d - c)$. This quadratic equation yields the explicit formulas for the two non-trivial eigenvalues, say α and α'.

The corresponding multiplicities, m and m', can be determined by combining the dimensional relation $1 + m + m' = n$ with the tracial relation $d + m\alpha + m'\alpha' = 0$. Solving this system, and using the explicit formulas for α and α', we are led to the desired explicit formulas for m and m'.

For the converse, let α and α' denote the non-trivial eigenvalues, and consider $M := A^2 - (\alpha + \alpha')A + \alpha\alpha'I$. We know that $(A - dI)M = 0$. This means that every column of M is an eigenvector for d, hence M is constant along columns. On the other hand, M is constant along the diagonal, by regularity. Thus M is a constant multiple of J, and strong regularity follows. Furthermore, we may read off the parameters from the relations $a - c = \alpha + \alpha'$ and $d - c = -\alpha\alpha'$. $\qquad\square$

Example 8.12. The Paley graph $P(q)$ has adjacency eigenvalues $\frac{1}{2}(\pm\sqrt{q} - 1)$, each with multiplicity $\frac{1}{2}(q - 1)$, as well as the simple eigenvalue $\frac{1}{2}(q - 1)$.

Example 8.13. The twin graphs have adjacency eigenvalues $-2, 2$, with multiplicities 9, 6, as well as the simple eigenvalue 6.

Example 8.14. The Petersen graph has adjacency eigenvalues $-2, 1$, with multiplicities 4, 5, as well as the simple eigenvalue 3.

Theorem 8.11 implies that the adjacency spectrum of a strongly regular graph is completely determined by its parameters. In particular, strongly regular graphs with the same parameters are isospectral. In this way, we get examples of isospectral but not isomorphic graphs, for instance the twin graphs, or the graphs provided by Corollary 3.23.

A more surprising upshot of Theorem 8.11 has to do with the multiplicities of the non-trivial eigenvalues. Namely, their integrality imposes strong restrictions on the parameters (n, d, a, c). There are two compatible possibilities, named according to the nature of the eigenvalues.

Quadratic type: $(n - 1)(a - c) + 2d = 0$. As $d < n - 1$, we must have $c - a = 1$ and $n - 1 = 2d$. Using Proposition 3.20, we then deduce that $2c = d$. Thus $(n, d, a, c) = (4c + 1, 2c, c - 1, c)$. The non-trivial eigenvalues are $\frac{1}{2}(-1 \pm \sqrt{n})$, so they are real quadratic integers, and they have equal multiplicities. The Paley graph $P(q)$ is of quadratic type.

Integral type: the discriminant disc is a square, say t^2, and t divides $(n - 1)(a - c) + 2d$. As t and $a - c$ have the same parity, the non-trivial eigenvalues $\frac{1}{2}(a - c \pm t)$ are integral. They have different multiplicities, unless we are in the quadratic type as well. The Petersen graph, the twin graphs, and $K_n \times K_n$ are of integral type.

8.3 Two gems

To illustrate just how useful the integrality of the multiplicities can be, let us consider two classical, but nevertheless striking, applications. Much of their appeal comes from the fact that we are establishing purely combinatorial results by exploiting spectral constraints!

Our first gem addresses a question we encountered in Section 2.2, that of classifying regular graphs of diameter 2 and girth 5.

Theorem 8.15 (Hoffman–Singleton). *If a regular graph has diameter 2 and girth 5, then the size and the degree are one of the following:* $n = 5$ *and* $d = 2$; $n = 10$ *and* $d = 3$; $n = 50$ *and* $d = 7$; $n = 3250$ *and* $d = 57$.

Proof. A regular graph with diameter 2 and girth 5 is strongly regular with parameters $a = 0$ and $c = 1$. Indeed, adjacent vertices have no common neighbours since there are no 3-cycles. Distinct non-adjacent vertices must have common neighbours, by the diameter assumption. There is in fact just one common neighbour, since there are no 4-cycles.

The only case of quadratic type is $(n, d) = (5, 2)$. Turning to the integral type, we let $t^2 = \text{disc} = 4d - 3$, so t divides $(n - 1) - 2d$. But $n = d^2 + 1$ by Proposition 3.20. Now t divides $4d - 3$ and $d^2 - 2d$, and simple arithmetic manipulations imply that t divides 15. If $t = 1$ then $d = 1$, which is impossible. The other possibilities, $t = 3$, $t = 5$, or $t = 15$, lead to (n, d) being one of $(10, 3)$, $(50, 7)$, $(3250, 57)$. $\square$

In the previous theorem, the first two cases are uniquely realized by two familiar graphs, the 5-cycle and the Petersen graph. It turns out that the third case, $n = 50$ and $d = 7$, is also realized by a unique graph — nowadays called the *Hoffman–Singleton graph.* Amazingly, it is still not known whether there is a graph realizing the last case, $n = 3250$ and $d = 57$.

Our second gem is often stated as the *friendship theorem*: if, in a group of people, any two persons have exactly one common friend, then there is a person who is everybody's friend. A more precise graph-theoretic statement is the following.

Theorem 8.16 (Erdős–Rényi–Sós). A graph with the property that any two distinct vertices have exactly one common neighbour, is a windmill graph.

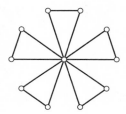

Figure 8.1.

Proof. We first consider the familiar context of regular graphs. If the given graph is complete, then it must be K_3. Otherwise, the graph is strongly regular with $a = c = 1$. Furthermore, it is of integral type. Let $t^2 = \text{disc} = 4(d-1)$, where t divides $2d$. Putting $t = 2t'$, we have that t' divides $d-1$ and d, hence $t' = 1$ and so $d = 2$. This means that our graph is a cycle, but then no cycle can have $a = 1$. We conclude that, in the regular case, the only possible graph is K_3 — the one-bladed windmill graph.

In the irregular case, the argument is combinatorial. We claim that there is a vertex w which is connected to every other vertex. It is then easy to conclude that the given graph is a windmill graph: for each v adjacent to w, there is a unique v' adjacent to w and to v, and so the vertices different from w are joined in disjoint pairs.

The crucial observation is that $\deg(u) = \deg(v)$ whenever u and v are non-adjacent vertices. Indeed, let $u_1, \ldots, u_k$ be the neighbours of u, and let v_i be the common neighbour of v and u_i. If $v_i = v_j$ for $i \neq j$, then that vertex and u have at least two common neighbours, namely u_i and u_j, and this is a contradiction. Thus $v_1, \ldots, v_k$ are distinct neighbours of v, hence $\deg(v) \geq \deg(u)$. Interchanging the roles of u and v, we get $\deg(u) = \deg(v)$, as desired.

Now let x and y be adjacent vertices having different degrees; they exist since we are assuming that the graph is irregular. The observation of the previous paragraph implies that every other vertex is adjacent to x or to y, possibly to both. If every vertex different from x is adjacent to x, or every vertex different from y is adjacent to y, then our claim is proved. Let us entertain for a moment the possibility that there are two vertices x' and y' such that x' is adjacent to x but not to y, and y' is adjacent to y but not to x. Let z be the common neighbour of x' and y'; note that $z \neq x, y$. Now z is adjacent to x or to y, say $z \sim y$. But then x and z have two common neighbours, namely x' and y. This is a contradiction.   □

Exercise 8.17. Show that the incidence graph $I_n(q)$ is not a bipartite double.

Notes. Theorem 8.15 is due to Hoffman and Singleton (*On Moore graphs with diameters 2 and 3*, IBM J. Res. Develop. 1960; Zbl 0096.38102). Theorem 8.16 is due to Erdős, Rényi, and Sós (*On a problem of graph theory*, Studia Sci. Math. Hungar. 1966; Zbl 0144.23302).

8.4 Design graphs

Recall that a design graph is a regular bipartite graph with the property that two distinct vertices of the same colour have the same number of common neighbours. The relevant parameters are m, the half-size; d, the degree; c, the number of neighbours shared by any monochromatic pair of vertices.

Theorem 8.18. A design graph has four distinct adjacency eigenvalues. In terms of the parameters (m, d, c), they are given as follows: $\pm\sqrt{d - c}$, each with multiplicity $m - 1$, and the simple eigenvalues $\pm d$.

Conversely, a regular bipartite graph having four distinct eigenvalues is a design graph.

Proof. As for any bipartite graph, the adjacency matrix of a design graph satisfies

$$A^2 = \begin{pmatrix} C_\bullet & 0 \\ 0 & C_\circ \end{pmatrix},$$

where $C_\bullet$ and $C_\circ$ are square matrices indexed by the black, respectively by the white, vertices. These two matrices have a simple combinatorial description: $C_\bullet$ and $C_\circ$ record, diagonally, the degrees in each colour, and off-diagonally the number of common neighbours for distinct vertices of the same colour.

The design property means that

$$C_\bullet = C_\circ = (d - c)I_m + cJ_m.$$

So the eigenvalues of both $C_\bullet$ and $C_\circ$ are $(d - c) + cm = d^2$ with multiplicity 1, and $d - c$ with multiplicity $m - 1$. The claim follows.

For the converse, let $\pm d$, $\pm \alpha$ be the distinct eigenvalues. As in the proof of Theorem 8.11, consider the matrix

$$M := (A + dI)(A^2 - \alpha^2 I) = A^3 + dA^2 - \alpha^2 A - d\alpha^2 I.$$

Then $(A - dI)M = 0$ and M is constant along the diagonal, so M is a constant multiple of J, say $M = kJ$. Now if u and v are two distinct vertices of the same colour, then $k = M(u, v) = dA^2(u, v)$. This is precisely the design property. □

Example 8.19. The incidence graph $I_n(q)$ is a design graph, with parameters

$$(m, d, c) = \Big(\frac{q^n - 1}{q - 1}, \frac{q^{n-1} - 1}{q - 1}, \frac{q^{n-2} - 1}{q - 1}\Big).$$

So the adjacency eigenvalues are $\pm(q^{n-1} - 1)/(q - 1)$ and $\pm q^{n/2-1}$.

Example 8.20. The bi-Paley graph $BP(q)$, where $q \equiv 3 \bmod 4$, is a design graph with parameters

$$(m, d, c) = \Big(q, \tfrac{1}{2}(q - 1), \tfrac{1}{4}(q - 3)\Big).$$

So the adjacency eigenvalues are $\pm\tfrac{1}{2}(q - 1)$ and $\pm\tfrac{1}{2}\sqrt{q + 1}$.

Design graphs with the same parameters are isospectral. For example, if $q = 2^n - 1$ is a Mersenne prime, where $n > 3$, then the bi-Paley graph $BP(q)$ and the incidence graph $I_n(2)$ are isospectral but not isomorphic.

Recall now that a partial design graph is a regular bipartite graph with the property that there are only two possible values for the number of neighbours shared by two vertices of the same colour. To a partial design graph with parameters (m, d, c_1, c_2) we associate a derived graph, the c_1-graph. This is the (possibly disconnected) graph on the m black vertices of the partial design graph, in which edges connect pairs of vertices that have exactly c_1 common neighbours. For instance, the Pappus graph, described in Example 1.7, is a partial design graph with parameters $(9, 3, 0, 1)$, and its 0-graph is a disconnected union of three 3-cycles.

The point is that the eigenvalues of a partial design graph can be computed from the eigenvalues of the derived graph which, quite often, is a much simpler graph. More precisely, we have the following theorem:

Theorem 8.21. Given a partial design graph with parameters (m, d, c_1, c_2), the following hold.

(i) The c_1-graph is regular of degree

$$d' = \frac{d(d - 1) - (m - 1)c_2}{c_1 - c_2}.$$

(ii) Let $\alpha_1' = d', \alpha_2', \ldots, \alpha_m'$ be the adjacency eigenvalues of the c_1-graph. Then the adjacency eigenvalues of the partial design graph are

$$\pm d, \quad \pm\sqrt{(d - c_2) + (c_1 - c_2)\alpha_k'} \quad (k = 2, \ldots, m).$$

The proof uses the following well-known fact:

Lemma 8.22. Let M and N be square matrices of the same size. Then MN and NM have the same eigenvalues.

Proof. We show that MN and NM have the same characteristic polynomial, that is, $\det(zI - MN) = \det(zI - NM)$ for each $z \in \mathbb{C}$. This is clear when $z = 0$. As for non-zero z, it suffices to treat the case $z = 1$. In the identity

$$\begin{pmatrix} I & 0 \\ N & I \end{pmatrix}\begin{pmatrix} I & M \\ 0 & I - NM \end{pmatrix} = \begin{pmatrix} I & M \\ N & I \end{pmatrix} = \begin{pmatrix} I - MN & M \\ 0 & I \end{pmatrix}\begin{pmatrix} I & 0 \\ N & I \end{pmatrix},$$

the determinant of the left-most product is $\det(I - NM)$, whereas for the right-most product it is $\det(I - MN)$.   □

Proof of Theorem 8.21. Let

$$A = \begin{pmatrix} 0 & B \\ B^t & 0 \end{pmatrix}$$

be the adjacency matrix of the partial design graph, where B is an $m \times m$ matrix. As in the case of design graphs, we consider the square of A:

$$A^2 = \begin{pmatrix} C_\bullet & 0 \\ 0 & C_\circ \end{pmatrix},$$

where $C_\bullet = BB^t$ and $C_\circ = B^t B$. The two matrices $C_\bullet$ and $C_\circ$ have the same eigenvalues, thanks to the previous lemma. Hence the eigenvalues of A are $\pm\sqrt{\mu}$ for μ running over the eigenvalues of $C_\bullet$. Each of $\pm\sqrt{\mu}$ has multiplicity equal to that of μ when $\mu \neq 0$. If $\mu = 0$, then 0 is an eigenvalue of A with twice the multiplicity of $\mu = 0$.

The characteristic property for a partial design means that the $m \times m$ matrix $C_\bullet$ can be expressed as follows. Its $(u_\bullet, v_\bullet)$-entry is d if $u_\bullet = v_\bullet$, c_1 if $u_\bullet$ and $v_\bullet$ are adjacent in the c_1-graph, c_2 if $u_\bullet$ and $v_\bullet$ are distinct and not adjacent in the c_1-graph. In short,

$$C_\bullet = (d - c_2)I + c_2 J + (c_1 - c_2)A',$$

where A' is the adjacency matrix of the c_1-graph.

(i) Thanks to regularity, A^2 has $\mathbb{1}$ as an eigenvector, with eigenvalue d^2. It follows, by restricting, that the same holds for $C_\bullet$. Applying the above expression for $C_\bullet$ to $\mathbb{1}$, we obtain

$$A'\mathbb{1} = \frac{d(d-1) - (m-1)c_2}{c_1 - c_2} \mathbb{1},$$

so the c_1-graph is regular, of degree d' equal to the coefficient on the right-hand side.

(ii) Let $f_1' = \mathbb{1}, f_2', \ldots, f_m'$ be an orthogonal basis of eigenvectors corresponding to the eigenvalues $\alpha_1' = d', \alpha_2', \ldots, \alpha_m'$ of A'. Then $C_\bullet f_1' = d^2 f_1'$, and

$$C_\bullet f_k' = \big((d - c_2) + (c_1 - c_2)\alpha_k'\big) f_k', \quad k = 2, \ldots, m,$$

since $J f_k' = 0$. Thus, the eigenvalues of $C_\bullet$ are d^2, and $(d - c_2) + (c_1 - c_2)\alpha_k'$ for $k = 2, \ldots, m$. We deduce that the eigenvalues of A are as claimed. □

Example 8.23. The Tutte–Coxeter graph, described in Example 3.29, is a partial design graph with parameters $(m, d, c_1, c_2) = (15, 3, 0, 1)$. The associated 0-graph is a regular graph of degree 8 on 15 vertices, which can be described as follows: the vertices are the edges of K_6, and two edges are adjacent when they share a common endpoint. This is, in fact, a strongly regular graph with parameters $a = c = 4$. We first find that the 0-graph has adjacency eigenvalues 8; 2 with multiplicity 5; -2 with multiplicity 9. Then, we deduce the adjacency eigenvalues of the Tutte–Coxeter graph: ±3; ±2, each with multiplicity 9; 0 with multiplicity 10.

Example 8.24. Recall that the cube graph Q_n is a partial design graph, with parameters $(m, d, c_1, c_2) = (2^{n-1}, n, 2, 0)$. The associated 2-graph is the halved cube graph $\frac{1}{2}Q_n$. This time, the derived graph is more complicated than the original design graph. We can then use Theorem 8.21 the other way around! We know, by Theorem 8.21, that $\frac{1}{2}Q_n$ has degree $\frac{1}{2}n(n-1)$, and that the non-trivial adjacency eigenvalues of Q_n are $\pm\sqrt{n + 2\alpha}$ for α running over the non-trivial adjacency eigenvalues of $\frac{1}{2}Q_n$. However, we also know, by easy arguments, that the non-trivial adjacency eigenvalues of Q_n are $n - 2k$ for $k = 1, \ldots, n - 1$; in other words, $\pm(n - 2k)$ for $k = 1, \ldots, \lfloor n/2 \rfloor$. We deduce that the non-trivial adjacency eigenvalues of $\frac{1}{2}Q_n$ are given by

$$\tfrac{1}{2}\big((n - 2k)^2 - n\big) = \tfrac{1}{2}n(n-1) - 2k(n-k)$$

for $k = 1, \ldots, \lfloor n/2 \rfloor$. This formula also works for $k = 0$, in which case it yields the degree. The Laplacian eigenvalues of $\frac{1}{2}Q_n$ are even nicer: $2k(n-k)$ for $k = 0, \ldots, \lfloor n/2 \rfloor$.

Exercise 8.25. Consider a linear space of dimension $n \geq 5$ over a field with q elements. Compute the adjacency eigenvalues of the following incidence graph: the vertices are the 2-spaces and the $(n-2)$-spaces, joined according to inclusion.

9

Largest eigenvalues

The focus of this chapter is on the largest adjacency eigenvalue $\alpha_{\max}$ and the largest Laplacian eigenvalue $\lambda_{\max}$.

9.1 Extremal eigenvalues of symmetric matrices

Both the adjacency matrix and the Laplacian matrix of a graph are real symmetric matrices. Let us discuss a simple principle governing the extremal eigenvalues of real symmetric matrices.

Let M be a real symmetric $n \times n$ matrix, with eigenvalues

$$\mu_{\min} = \mu_1 \le \cdots \le \mu_n = \mu_{\max}.$$

Note that the indexing of the Laplacian eigenvalues conforms with the above ordering, but the adjacency eigenvalues run backwards.

The following result characterizes the extremal eigenvalues as extremal values of the *Rayleigh ratio*

$$R(f) := \frac{\langle Mf, f \rangle}{\langle f, f \rangle},$$

where $0 \ne f \in \mathbb{C}^n$. Note that the Rayleigh ratio is real valued.

Theorem 9.1. We have

$$\mu_{\min} = \min_{f \ne 0} R(f), \qquad \mu_{\max} = \max_{f \ne 0} R(f),$$

and the extremal values are attained precisely on the corresponding eigenvectors.

Proof. Let $f_1, f_2, \ldots, f_n$ be an orthonormal basis of eigenvectors. Decomposing $f \ne 0$ as $f = \sum c_i f_i$, we have $Mf = \sum \mu_i c_i f_i$, so

$$R(f) = \frac{\langle Mf, f \rangle}{\langle f, f \rangle} = \frac{\sum \mu_i |c_i|^2}{\sum |c_i|^2}.$$

Hence $\mu_{\min} \le R(f) \le \mu_{\max}$. If f is an eigenvector for $\mu_{\min}$ then $R(f) = \mu_{\min}$, and similarly for $\mu_{\max}$. Conversely, if $R(f)$ equals, say, $\mu_{\min}$, then $c_i = 0$ whenever $\mu_i \ne \mu_{\min}$. Thus f is in the $\mu_{\min}$-eigenspace. $\square$

Despite its simple proof, the above spectral principle turns out to be very useful. In Section 10.1 we will generalize it by providing similar descriptions, in terms of the Rayleigh ratio, for all the eigenvalues not just the extremal ones.

9.2 Largest adjacency eigenvalue

Theorem 9.2. The adjacency eigenvalue $\alpha_{\max}$ is simple, and it has a positive eigen-function.

This theorem is the single most important fact about $\alpha_{\max}$. Let us explain it, prove it, and then use it to derive a number of consequences.

A function on a graph is *positive* if all its values are positive. On the Laplacian side, we know that $\lambda_{\min} = 0$ is a simple eigenvalue, and it has a positive eigenfunction — namely, the constant function $\mathbb{1}$. Theorem 9.2 should be seen as an adjacency dual of this Laplacian fact.

Proof. Let f be an eigenfunction of $\alpha_{\max}$. We claim that $|f|$ is a positive eigenfunction of $\alpha_{\max}$. We have

$$\langle A|f|, |f| \rangle = \sum_{u \sim v} |f|(u)|f|(v) \geq \left| \sum_{u \sim v} f(u)\bar{f}(v) \right| = |\langle Af, f \rangle|$$

and

$$|\langle Af, f \rangle| = |\alpha_{\max}\langle f, f \rangle| = \alpha_{\max}\langle f, f \rangle = \alpha_{\max}\langle |f|, |f| \rangle.$$

Here we are using the fact that $\alpha_{\max} \geq 0$; this follows from $\sum \alpha_k = 0$.

Therefore $\langle A|f|, |f| \rangle = \alpha_{\max}\langle |f|, |f| \rangle$, so $|f|$ is indeed an eigenfunction of $\alpha_{\max}$. To show that $|f|$ is positive, consider the eigenrelation

$$\sum_{u:u \sim v} |f|(u) = \alpha_{\max}|f|(v).$$

If $|f|$ vanishes at a vertex, then $|f|$ vanishes at each one of its neighbours. Thus, vanishing is contagious, but then connectivity would imply that $|f| \equiv 0$, a contradiction. In addition, the inequality $\sum_{u \sim v} |f|(u)|f|(v) \geq \left| \sum_{u \sim v} f(u)\bar{f}(v) \right|$ we used along the way must be an equality. Now, if $\{z_j\}$ are complex numbers satisfying $\left| \sum z_j \right| = \sum |z_j|$, then they have the same phase: there is $\omega \in \mathbb{C}$ with $|\omega| = 1$ such that $z_j = \omega|z_j|$ for all j. In our case, $f(u)\bar{f}(v) = \omega|f(u)||f(v)|$ or

$$\frac{f(u)}{|f(u)|} = \omega\frac{f(v)}{|f(v)|} \tag{9.1}$$

whenever u and v are adjacent. As f and $|f|$ are eigenfunctions of $\alpha_{\max}$, we have

$$\alpha_{\max} f(v) = \sum_{u:u\sim v} f(u) = \omega \frac{f(v)}{|f(v)|} \sum_{u:u\sim v} |f(u)| = \omega \frac{f(v)}{|f(v)|} \alpha_{\max} |f(v)| = \omega \alpha_{\max} f(v),$$

for an arbitrarily fixed vertex v. Thus $\omega = 1$, and (9.1) says that $f/|f|$ is constant across edges. Thanks to connectivity, it follows that $f/|f|$ is a constant. In other words, f is a scalar multiple of a positive function.

We may now conclude that the eigenspace of $\alpha_{\max}$ is one-dimensional. Otherwise, we could pick two orthogonal eigenfunctions f and g. Up to rescaling, we could also assume f and g positive. But then $0 = \langle f, g \rangle = \sum f(v)g(v)$ provides a contradiction, as every term on the right-hand side is positive. □

One upshot of this theorem is that it provides a tool for recognizing the largest adjacency eigenvalue. This is an intrinsic certificate, in the sense that we do not need to know the other eigenvalues!

Corollary 9.3. The only adjacency eigenvalue admitting a positive eigenfunction is $\alpha_{\max}$.

Proof. Distinct eigenvalues have orthogonal eigenfunctions. Two orthogonal functions cannot both be positive. □

Example 9.4. Consider a bipartite graph which is *biregular*, in the sense that black vertices have equal degree, say $d_\bullet$, and white vertices have equal degree, say $d_\circ$. The function that equals $\sqrt{d_\bullet}$ at each black vertex, respectively $\sqrt{d_\circ}$ at each white vertex, is an adjacency eigenfunction, with eigenvalue $\sqrt{d_\bullet d_\circ}$. As the eigenfunction is positive, we deduce that $\sqrt{d_\bullet d_\circ} = \alpha_{\max}$.

The next corollary concerns the smallest adjacency eigenvalue. We already know that $0 \geq \alpha_{\min} \geq -d$, but now we can say a bit more.

Corollary 9.5. We have $\alpha_{\min} \geq -\alpha_{\max}$, with equality if and only if the graph is bipartite.

Note that the implication '$\alpha_{\min} = -\alpha_{\max}$ implies bipartite' improves the implication 'symmetric adjacency spectrum implies bipartite' we already had.

First proof. We adapt the proof of Theorem 9.2. Let f be an eigenfunction of $\alpha_{\min}$, and consider $|f|$. Then

$$\langle A|f|, |f| \rangle = \sum_{u\sim v} |f|(u)|f|(v) \geq \left| \sum_{u\sim v} f(u)\bar{f}(v) \right| = |\langle Af, f \rangle| = -\alpha_{\min} \langle |f|, |f| \rangle.$$

Therefore $\alpha_{\max} \geq -\alpha_{\min}$. Now let us analyze the case of equality. Firstly, $|f|$ has to be an eigenfunction of $\alpha_{\max}$, in particular f never vanishes. Secondly, we have

(9.1) once again. Adjacency being a symmetric relation, we must have $\omega = \pm 1$. If $\omega = 1$, then f is a scalar multiple of $|f|$. Hence f is an eigenfunction of $\alpha_{\max}$, a contradiction. Thus $\omega = -1$. This means that $f/|f|$ switches sign across each edge, and we get a bipartition of our graph. □

Second proof. Let $r \geq 1$ be odd. Then

$$0 \leq \operatorname{Tr} A^r = \sum \alpha_k^r \leq \alpha_{\min}^r + (n-1)\alpha_{\max}^r,$$

so

$$(n-1)\alpha_{\max}^r \geq (-\alpha_{\min})^r.$$

Taking the rth root, and letting $r \to \infty$, we obtain $\alpha_{\max} \geq -\alpha_{\min}$. Assume now that equality holds, $\alpha_{\max} = -\alpha_{\min}$. If the graph is non-bipartite, then the largest adjacency eigenvalue of its bipartite double is not simple — a contradiction. □

Notes. Part of what we said about the extremal adjacency eigenvalues falls under the scope of Perron–Frobenius theory. The aspect that is relevant for our discussion concerns square matrices M that are non-negative, in the sense that $M(i, j) \geq 0$ for each i, j, and irreducible, meaning that for each i, j there is some $k \geq 0$ such that $M^k(i, j) > 0$. A symmetric non-negative $n \times n$ matrix M has an associated underlying graph: the vertex set is $\{1, \ldots, n\}$, and $i \neq j$ are connected if $M(i, j) > 0$. Loops can be added as well, to account for positive diagonal entries. Irreducibility of M then corresponds to connectivity of the underlying graph. Conversely, consider a connected graph, possibly with loops, in which edges have positive weights. Then the accordingly weighted adjacency matrix is a symmetric, non-negative, irreducible matrix. Adjacency results established above can be extended as follows. Let M be a symmetric, non-negative, irreducible $n \times n$ matrix. Then (i) the largest eigenvalue $\mu_{\max}$ is simple, and it has a positive eigenvector, and (ii) the smallest eigenvalue satisfies $\mu_{\min} \geq -\mu_{\max}$.

9.3 The average degree

The average vertex degree of a graph is denoted d_{ave}, and it is given, as the name suggests, by

$$d_{\mathrm{ave}} = \frac{1}{n} \sum_v \deg(v).$$

Using this notion, we can sharpen the already known fact that $\alpha_{\max} \leq d$.

Theorem 9.6. We have $d_{\mathrm{ave}} \leq \alpha_{\max} \leq d$, with equality on either side if and only if the graph is regular.

The above double bound for α_{max} suggests that it can be interpreted as a spectral notion of degree.

Proof. Let f be a positive eigenfunction of α_{max}. Then $\alpha_{max} f(v) = \sum_{u:u \sim v} f(u)$ for each vertex v and, adding all these relations, we get

$$\alpha_{max} \sum f(v) = \sum \deg(v) f(v) \le d \sum f(v).$$

Hence $\alpha_{max} \le d$, with equality if and only if $\deg(v) = d$ for each v, that is, the graph is regular.

For the constant function $\mathbb{1}$, the Rayleigh ratio is

$$\frac{\langle A\mathbb{1}, \mathbb{1} \rangle}{\langle \mathbb{1}, \mathbb{1} \rangle} = \frac{\sum \deg(v)}{n} = d_{ave},$$

so $d_{ave} \le \alpha_{max}$. If equality holds then $\mathbb{1}$ is an eigenfunction for α_{max}, and so the graph must be regular. $\qquad\square$

Corollary 9.7. The regularity of a graph can be read off from its adjacency spectrum.

Proof. A spectral criterion for regularity is that $\alpha_{max} = d_{ave}$. But the average degree is determined by the spectrum:

$$d_{ave} = \frac{1}{n} \sum \alpha_k^2$$

So, given the adjacency spectrum of a graph, it can be checked whether the graph is regular by verifying whether the relation $\sum \alpha_k^2 = n\alpha_{max}$ holds. $\qquad\square$

Exercise 9.8. Show that

$$\sum |\alpha_k| \le \tfrac{1}{2} n(\sqrt{n} + 1)$$

and discuss the case of equality.

Sometimes the list of *distinct* adjacency eigenvalues suffices for hearing regularity. The following result illustrates this idea. Let us recall that an extremal design graph of degree d has adjacency eigenvalues $\pm d$ and $\pm\sqrt{d-1}$.

Theorem 9.9. Assume that the distinct adjacency eigenvalues of a graph are $\pm \alpha$ and $\pm\sqrt{\alpha - 1}$, where $\alpha \ge 3$. Then the graph is an extremal design graph, of degree $d = \alpha$.

Proof. The extremal adjacency eigenvalues have opposite signs, so the graph is bipartite. We aim to show that the graph is also regular. For then we will be able to conclude by applying Theorem 8.18. We show regularity by arguing that α, the largest adjacency eigenvalue, equals the average degree d_{ave}.

Since the eigenvalues of A are $\pm\alpha$, $\pm\sqrt{\alpha-1}$, we have $(A^2-\alpha^2 I)(A^2-(\alpha-1)I)=0$ and so $A^4=(\alpha^2+\alpha-1)A^2-\alpha^2(\alpha-1)I$. Taking traces, we get

$$\operatorname{Tr}(A^4)=(\alpha^2+\alpha-1)nd_{\text{ave}}-\alpha^2(\alpha-1)n.$$

On the other, we may understand $\operatorname{Tr}(A^4)$ in a combinatorial way. If u is a vertex, then

$$A^4(u,u)=c_4(u)+\deg(u)^2+\sum_{v:v\sim u}\big(\deg(v)-1\big),$$

where the first term counts the 4-cycles starting and ending at u, the second term counts the closed paths of the form $u\sim v\sim u\sim v'\sim u$, and the third counts the closed paths of the form $u\sim v\sim w(\neq u)\sim v\sim u$. Therefore,

$$\operatorname{Tr}(A^4)=c_4+\sum_u\deg(u)^2+\sum_u\sum_{v:v\sim u}\deg(v)-\sum_u\deg(u)$$

$$=c_4+2\sum_u\deg(u)^2-\sum_u\deg(u),$$

where c_4 denotes the number of based 4-cycles in the graph. Now $\sum\deg(u)=nd_{\text{ave}}$, and we can safely bound

$$\sum\deg(u)^2\geq\frac{1}{n}\Big(\sum\deg(u)\Big)^2=nd_{\text{ave}}^2$$

as we expect the graph to be regular. Furthermore, we disregard the c_4 term since the girth of our graph should be 6. In summary, we have the following combinatorial bound:

$$\operatorname{Tr}(A^4)\geq 2nd_{\text{ave}}^2-nd_{\text{ave}}.$$

Combining this bound with the previous computation of $\operatorname{Tr}(A^4)$, we deduce

$$(\alpha^2+\alpha-1)d_{\text{ave}}-\alpha^2(\alpha-1)\geq 2d_{\text{ave}}^2-d_{\text{ave}},$$

that is,

$$(d_{\text{ave}}-\alpha)(\alpha^2-\alpha-2d_{\text{ave}})\geq 0.$$

Here $\alpha\geq d_{\text{ave}}$ and $\alpha^2-\alpha\geq 2\alpha\geq 2d_{\text{ave}}$, as $\alpha\geq 3$. So it must be that $\alpha=d_{\text{ave}}$.   □

Exercise 9.10. Show that a graph whose adjacency eigenvalues are -2, 1, 3 must be the Petersen graph. True or false: a graph whose Laplacian eigenvalues are 0, 2, 5 must be the Petersen graph.

Notes. The bound in Exercise 9.8 is due to Koolen and Moulton (*Maximal energy graphs*, Adv. Appl. Math. 2001; Zbl 0976.05040). The expression $\sum|\alpha_k|$ is called the energy of a graph, and it is motivated by considerations in theoretical chemistry.

9.4 A spectral Turán theorem

The following theorem is a true classic. A whole subfield, that of extremal graph theory, originates from this highly influential result.

Theorem 9.11 (Turán). If a graph on n vertices does not contain the complete graph K_{k+1} as a subgraph, then the number of edges can be bounded as

$$|E| \leq \frac{1}{2}\left(1 - \frac{1}{k}\right)n^2.$$

Recall that $\alpha_{\max} \geq d_{\text{ave}} = 2|E|/n$. So the next theorem can be viewed as a spectral enhancement of Turán's theorem.

Theorem 9.12 (Wilf). If a graph on n vertices does not contain K_{k+1} as a subgraph, then its largest adjacency eigenvalue satisfies the following upper bound:

$$\alpha_{\max} \leq \left(1 - \frac{1}{k}\right)n.$$

The key ingredient in the proof is the following elegant fact, interesting in its own right.

Lemma 9.13 (Motzkin–Straus). Consider a graph which does not contain K_{k+1} as a subgraph. Let f be a non-negative function on the vertices, satisfying $\sum_v f(v) = 1$. Then

$$\sum_{u \sim v} f(u)f(v) \leq 1 - \frac{1}{k}.$$

Proof. Consider the support graph of f, that is to say, the subgraph induced by those vertices where f is non-zero. If the support graph is complete, then it has at most k vertices. In this case, we have

$$\langle Af, f \rangle = \sum_{u \neq v} f(u)f(v) = \left(\sum_v f(v)\right)^2 - \left(\sum_v f(v)^2\right) = 1 - \sum_v f(v)^2$$

and, by Cauchy–Schwarz,

$$\sum_v f(v)^2 \geq \frac{1}{k}\left(\sum_v f(v)\right)^2 = \frac{1}{k}.$$

This establishes the desired bound in the complete case.

Assume now that the support graph of f is not complete. The plan is to 'flow' f towards the complete case. Let x and y be distinct, non-adjacent support vertices, and modify the weight distribution by transferring the weight of y to x. Namely, define f' as follows: $f'(y) = 0$, $f'(x) = f(x) + f(y)$, and $f'(z) = f(z)$ for all other vertices. Thus f' also has non-negative entries, and satisfies $\sum_v f'(v) = 1$, but it has smaller support. We wish to compare $\langle Af', f' \rangle$ to $\langle Af, f \rangle$. To that end, it is convenient to write $f' = f + \epsilon$, where ϵ is the perturbation given by $\epsilon(x) = f(y)$, $\epsilon(y) = -f(y)$, and $\epsilon = 0$ elsewhere. Now

$$\langle Af', f' \rangle = \langle Af, f \rangle + \langle Af, \epsilon \rangle + \langle A\epsilon, f \rangle + \langle A\epsilon, \epsilon \rangle = \langle Af, f \rangle + 2\langle Af, \epsilon \rangle,$$

so

$$\tfrac{1}{2}\left(\langle Af', f' \rangle - \langle Af, f \rangle\right) = \langle Af, \epsilon \rangle = \epsilon(x)Af(x) + \epsilon(y)Af(y)$$
$$= f(y)\left(Af(x) - Af(y)\right).$$

This gives us the rule for deciding which one of the two non-adjacent vertices is the weight receiver: we transfer the weight of y to x when $Af(x) \geq Af(y)$. Under this rule, $\langle Af', f' \rangle \geq \langle Af, f \rangle$. This means that, as long as the support graph is non-complete, we may shrink the support without decreasing the quantity we are interested in. After performing this procedure a finite number of times, we reach a support graph which is complete.   □

Turán's theorem follows from the lemma, by taking f to be constant, that is, $f(v) = 1/n$ for each vertex v. The idea of its spectral strengthening is to use a better choice for f.

Proof of Theorem 9.12. Let f be a positive eigenfunction of $\alpha_{\max}$. The previous lemma yields

$$\langle Af, f \rangle = \sum_{u \sim v} f(u)f(v) \leq \left(1 - \frac{1}{k}\right)\left(\sum_v f(v)\right)^2.$$

Now $\langle Af, f \rangle = \alpha_{\max} \langle f, f \rangle$, and

$$\left(\sum_v f(v)\right)^2 \leq n \sum_v f(v)^2 = n \langle f, f \rangle.$$

The desired bound follows.   □

Notes. Turán's theorem (*On an extremal problem in graph theory*, Mat. Fiz. Lapok 1941, in Hungarian, Zbl 0026.26903; *On the theory of graphs*, Colloquium Math. 1954 in English, Zbl 0055.17004) is actually a bit sharper, and it says the following: among all graphs with n vertices that do not contain K_{k+1}, there is an explicit 'Turán graph' Tu(n, k) having the largest number of edges. The graph Tu(n, k) is the complete multipartite graph obtained by partitioning n vertices into k subsets as evenly as possible. A concrete formula for the number of edges of $\text{Tu}(n, k)$ can be easily written down, but it is somewhat cumbersome. The weaker bound stated above, $\frac{1}{2}(1 - \frac{1}{k})n^2$, is convenient and essentially sharp, for it is attained when k divides n. The case $k = 2$ of Turán's theorem is an early result of Mantel (1906), and it appeared as Exercise 1.2 in this text.

Theorem 9.12 is due to Wilf (*Spectral bounds for the clique and independence numbers of graphs*, J. Combin. Theory Ser. B 1986; Zbl 0598.05047). The key lemma is a result of Motzkin and Straus (*Maxima for graphs and a new proof of a theorem of Turán*, Canad. J. Math. 1965; Zbl 0129.39902).

9.5 Largest Laplacian eigenvalue of bipartite graphs

Consider a bipartite graph. Then its adjacency spectrum is symmetric with respect to 0, so $\alpha_{\min}$ is a simple eigenvalue. Furthermore, $\alpha_{\min}$ has an eigenfunction that takes positive values on one side of the bipartition, and negative values on the other side of the bipartition. Such a function is said to be *alternating*. These facts have a Laplacian dual.

Theorem 9.14. The Laplacian eigenvalue $\lambda_{\max}$ is simple, and it has an alternating eigenfunction.

Proof. The argument is similar to the one of Theorem 9.2. Let g be an eigenfunction for $\lambda_{\max}$. Define g' by $g' = |g|$ on $V_\bullet$, respectively $g' = -|g|$ on $V_\circ$. We claim that g' is an alternating eigenfunction of $\lambda_{\max}$. For each edge $\{u, v\}$, we have $|g'(u) - g'(v)| = |g(u)| + |g(v)| \geq |g(u) - g(v)|$. Consequently,

$$\langle Lg', g' \rangle = \sum_{\{u,v\} \in E} |g'(u) - g'(v)|^2 \geq \sum_{\{u,v\} \in E} |g(u) - g(v)|^2 = \langle Lg, g \rangle.$$

Also,

$$\langle Lg, g \rangle = \lambda_{\max} \langle g, g \rangle = \lambda_{\max} \langle g', g' \rangle,$$

since $|g| = |g'|$. Hence $\langle Lg', g' \rangle = \lambda_{\max} \langle g', g' \rangle$, and it follows that g' is an eigenfunction for $\lambda_{\max}$. Next, we use the eigenrelation for g' to argue that g' never vanishes. For each vertex v we have

$$\sum_{u:u\sim v} g'(u) = (\deg(v) - \lambda_{\max})g'(v).$$

In addition, $g'(u)$ does not change sign as u runs over the neighbours of v. So, if $g'(v) = 0$ then $g'(u) = 0$ for each neighbour u of v, and then connectivity leads us to the contradiction $g \equiv 0$.

Moreover, we must have $|g(u)| + |g(v)| = |g(u) - g(v)|$ for every edge $\{u, v\}$. This means that the complex numbers $g(u)$ and $g(v)$ are collinear with, and on opposite sides of, the origin 0. In other words,

$$\frac{g(u)}{|g(u)|} + \frac{g(v)}{|g(v)|} = 0$$

for every edge $\{u, v\}$. It follows that, for some non-zero scalar c, $g/|g| = c$ on $V_{\bullet}$ and $g/|g| = -c$ on $V_{\circ}$. Thus g is a scalar multiple of g', an alternating function.

We deduce that the eigenspace of $\lambda_{\max}$ is one-dimensional. The reason is that two orthogonal functions, say f and g, cannot both be alternating: in the expansion

$$\langle f, g \rangle = \sum f(v_{\bullet})g(v_{\bullet}) + \sum f(v_{\circ})g(v_{\circ}),$$

all terms have one and the same sign. $\square$

The observation that two orthogonal functions cannot both be alternating also provides a way of recognizing $\lambda_{\max}$ without knowing the full Laplacian spectrum. The intrinsic certificate is provided, again, by the eigenfunction.

Corollary 9.15. The only Laplacian eigenvalue with an alternating eigenfunction is $\lambda_{\max}$.

Example 9.16. Consider a biregular bipartite graph, with vertex degrees $d_{\bullet}$ and $d_{\circ}$. Let $m_{\bullet}$ and $m_{\circ}$ denote the number of black, respectively white vertices, and note that $d_{\bullet}m_{\bullet} = d_{\circ}m_{\circ}$. Then the function which equals m_0 at each black vertex, respectively $-m_{\bullet}$ at each white vertex, is a Laplacian eigenfunction, with eigenvalue $d_{\bullet} + d_{\circ}$. Since the eigenfunction is alternating, it follows that $d_{\bullet} + d_{\circ} = \lambda_{\max}$.

9.6 Subgraphs

How do eigenvalues change upon passing to subgraphs? The next result addresses the behaviour of the largest eigenvalues. We will return to this question later on, with results pertaining to the entire spectrum.

Theorem 9.17. Let X' be a proper subgraph of a graph X. Then the largest eigenvalues satisfy $\alpha'_{\max} < \alpha_{\max}$, and $\lambda'_{\max} \leq \lambda_{\max}$.

Proof. Let f' be a positive eigenfunction for $\alpha'_{\max}$. Extend f', originally defined on the vertex subset V', to a function f on V by setting $f \equiv 0$ outside V'. Then $\langle f', f' \rangle = \langle f, f \rangle$, and

$$\langle A'f', f' \rangle = 2 \sum_{\{u,v\} \in E'} f'(u)f'(v) \leq 2 \sum_{\{u,v\} \in E} f'(u)f'(v) = \langle Af, f \rangle.$$

Hence

$$\alpha'_{\max} = \frac{\langle A'f', f'\rangle}{\langle f', f'\rangle} \le \frac{\langle Af, f\rangle}{\langle f, f\rangle} \le \alpha_{\max}.$$

If $\alpha'_{\max} = \alpha_{\max}$ then equalities hold throughout the above estimate. On the one hand, f is an eigenfunction for $\alpha_{\max}$. In particular, f never vanishes so $V' = V$. On the other hand, it follows that $E' = E$. Therefore X' is X itself, contradicting the properness assumption.

The argument for the largest Laplacian eigenvalue is similar, though easier. Let g' be an eigenfunction for $\lambda'_{\max}$, and extend it to a function g on X by setting $g \equiv 0$ off the vertices of X'. Then $\langle g', g'\rangle = \langle g, g\rangle$ and

$$\langle L'g', g'\rangle = \sum_{\{u,v\}\in E'} |g'(u) - g'(v)|^2 \le \sum_{\{u,v\}\in E} |g(u) - g(v)|^2 = \langle Lg, g\rangle.$$

Taking Rayleigh ratios, it follows that $\lambda'_{\max} \le \lambda_{\max}$. □

Exercise 9.18. Show that $\lambda_{\max} \ge d + 1$ and $\alpha_{\max} \ge \sqrt{d}$. Describe, in each case, the graphs for which equality holds.

The following result, a rather striking classification, combines the adjacency part of Theorem 9.17 with Corollary 9.3.

Theorem 9.19 (Smith). The graphs satisfying $\alpha_{\max} < 2$ are the A-D-E graphs of Figure 9.1. The graphs satisfying $\alpha_{\max} = 2$ are the extended A-D-E graphs of Figure 9.2.

Proof. The extended A-D-E graphs have $\alpha_{\max} = 2$. A fun exercise, left to the reader, shows that each graph admits 2 as an adjacency eigenvalue, and the corresponding eigenfunction has positive (and integral) entries. It follows that 2 is, indeed, the largest adjacency eigenvalue.

The A-D-E graphs have $\alpha_{\max} < 2$. Indeed, they are proper subgraphs of the extended A-D-E graphs in the way suggested by the notation.

Now consider a graph X with $\alpha_{\max} \le 2$. If X contains one of the extended A-D-E graphs as a subgraph, then the subgraph must be the whole of X. So let us pursue the case when none of the extended A-D-E graphs appear as a subgraph of X; we wish to show that X is one of the A-D-E graphs.

To begin with, X is a tree since it contains no cycle $\tilde{A}_n$. A degenerate instance of $\tilde{D}_n$ is a star with 4 pendant vertices; using it, we infer that the maximal vertex degree in X is at most 3. Another use of $\tilde{D}_n$ tells us that at most one vertex has degree 3. One possibility is that X is a path, A_n in our list. Otherwise, there is precisely one trivalent vertex in X. To figure out the length of the three pending paths, we use the graphs $\tilde{E}_6$, $\tilde{E}_7$, and $\tilde{E}_8$. The first tells us that at least one of the paths has length 1.

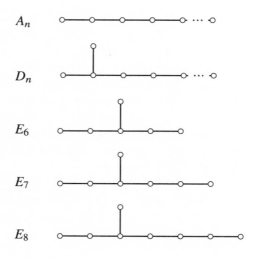

Figure 9.1. The A-D-E graphs.

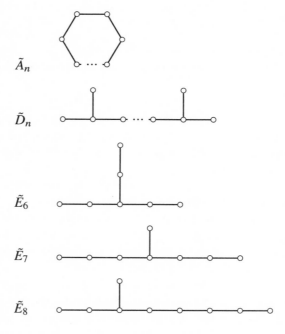

Figure 9.2. The extended A-D-E graphs.

Assume that there is precisely one such path, otherwise we are in the D_n case. Using $\tilde{E}_7$, we deduce that at least one of the remaining two paths has length 2. The third path can have length 2, 3, or 4, but no larger, because of $\tilde{E}_8$. So X is one of E_6, E_7, or E_8. $\qquad\qquad\square$

Notes. Theorem 9.19 is due to John H. Smith (*Some properties of the spectrum of a graph*, in 'Combinatorial structures and their applications', Gordon and Breach 1970; Zbl 0249.05136). The A-D-E graphs and their extended versions are also known as the simple Coxeter–Dynkin diagrams and they occur, quite amazingly, in several classification results for seemingly unrelated objects. A few words about the notation in Figures 9.1 and 9.2. The number of vertices of a graph is given by the index in Figure 9.1, and by the index plus 1 in Figure 9.2. The notation for the A-type, standard in this context, is slightly at odds with some of our notation: $\tilde{A}_n$ is the cycle C_{n+1}, while A_n is not an Andrásfai graph but a path graph, and should be denoted P_n.

9.7 Largest eigenvalues of trees

Consider a rooted tree, that is, a tree with a distinguished vertex. A function on the vertices of the tree is *radial* if it is constant on spheres around the root vertex. The rooted tree is *radially regular* if the degree function is radial. Two important examples are the trees $T_{d,R}$ and $\tilde{T}_{d,R}$. Recall that the root vertex has degree $d-1$ in $T_{d,R}$, and degree d in $\tilde{T}_{d,R}$; the pendant vertices lie on a sphere of radius R about the root; the remaining intermediate vertices all have degree d.

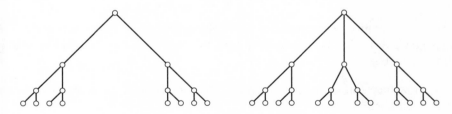

Figure 9.3. $T_{3,3}$ and $\tilde{T}_{3,3}$, once again.

Lemma 9.20. For a radially regular tree, the adjacency and the Laplacian eigenfunctions corresponding to the largest eigenvalues are radial.

Proof. For a function f defined on the vertices of the tree, we let $f^{\#}$ denote the radial function obtained by averaging f on spheres about the root vertex. More precisely, we define $f^{\#}$ on S_r by

$$f_r^{\#} \equiv \frac{1}{|S_r|} \sum_{v \in S_r} f(v),$$

where S_r, for $r = 0, 1, \ldots, R$, denotes the sphere of radius r with respect to the root. We claim that the adjacency and the Laplacian operators commute with averaging:

$$(Af)^{\#} = A(f^{\#}), \qquad (Lf)^{\#} = L(f^{\#}).$$

The claim implies that averaging turns eigenfunctions into radial eigenfunctions, except when averaging yields the zero function. This degeneration cannot happen for the largest eigenvalues, since $\alpha_{\max}$ admits a positive eigenfunction, whereas $\lambda_{\max}$ admits an alternating eigenfunction — say, positive on even-radius spheres and negative on odd-radius spheres. As the eigenfunctions of $\alpha_{\max}$ and $\lambda_{\max}$ are unique up to scaling, we conclude that they are radial.

Now let us prove the claim. It suffices to check that $A(f^{\#}) = (Af)^{\#}$ on each sphere. As the degree function is constant on spheres, the same holds for the Laplacian. Note that $A(f^{\#})$ is constant on a sphere of radius r, namely

$$A(f^{\#}) \equiv f_{r-1}^{\#} + \frac{|S_{r+1}|}{|S_r|} f_{r+1}^{\#} \quad \text{on } S_r.$$

But the right-hand quantity is precisely $(Af)_r^{\#}$, thanks to the following computation:

$$|S_r|(Af)_r^{\#} = \sum_{v \in S_r} (Af)(v) = \frac{|S_r|}{|S_{r-1}|} \sum_{u \in S_{r-1}} f(u) + \sum_{w \in S_{r+1}} f(w)$$

$$= |S_r| f_{r-1}^{\#} + |S_{r+1}| f_{r+1}^{\#}.$$

A natural convention accommodates the extreme cases, $r = 0$ (the root) and $r = R$ (the pendant vertices). The reader who feels that they should be handled separately is invited to do so.   □

We now focus on the tree $T_{d,R}$, and we determine the eigenvalues that admit a radial eigenfunction.

Lemma 9.21. The adjacency eigenvalues of $T_{d,R}$ that admit a radial eigenfunction are

$$\left\{ 2\sqrt{d-1} \cos \frac{\pi k}{R+2} : k = 1, \ldots, R+1 \right\}.$$

The Laplacian eigenvalues of $T_{d,R}$ that admit a radial eigenfunction are

$$\left\{ 0, d - 2\sqrt{d-1} \cos \frac{\pi k}{R+1} : k = 1, \ldots, R \right\}.$$

Proof. Let α be an adjacency eigenvalue admitting a radial eigenfunction f. If f_r denotes the value on the sphere of radius r, then

$$\alpha f_0 = (d-1)f_1,$$
$$\alpha f_r = f_{r-1} + (d-1)f_{r+1}, \quad r = 1, \ldots, R-1,$$
$$\alpha f_R = f_{R-1}.$$

The solution to this recurrence is a linear combination $f_r = ax_1^{r+1} + bx_2^{r+1}$, where x_1 and x_2 are the roots of the equation $(d-1)x^2 - \alpha x + 1 = 0$, subject to the initial and terminal conditions $f_{-1} = 0$, $f_{R+1} = 0$. Thus $a + b = 0$ and $x_1^{R+2} = x_2^{R+2}$. Since $x_1 x_2 = 1/(d-1)$, we find that $x_1 = \zeta/\sqrt{d-1}$ and $x_2 = \bar{\zeta}/\sqrt{d-1}$, where ζ satisfies $\zeta^{2(R+2)} = 1$. Then

$$\alpha = (d-1)(x_1 + x_2) = 2\sqrt{d-1}\,\mathrm{Re}(\zeta).$$

Up to multiplication by a scalar, f is given by

$$f_r = (d-1)^{-r/2}\,\mathrm{Im}(\zeta^{r+1}), \quad r = 0, \ldots, R.$$

For f to be non-zero, we have to have $\zeta \neq \pm 1$. Conversely, if $\zeta \neq \pm 1$ then f is non-zero since $f_0 \neq 0$. We conclude that the adjacency eigenvalues admitting radial eigenfunctions are

$$\left\{2\sqrt{d-1}\,\mathrm{Re}(\zeta) : \zeta^{2(R+2)} = 1, \zeta \neq \pm 1\right\}.$$

Now let λ be a Laplacian eigenvalue admitting a radial eigenfunction g. If g_r denotes, again, the value on the sphere of radius r, then

$$(d-1-\lambda)g_0 = (d-1)g_1,$$
$$(d-\lambda)g_r = g_{r-1} + (d-1)g_{r+1}, \quad r = 1, \ldots, R-1,$$
$$(1-\lambda)g_R = g_{R-1}.$$

The solution is given by $g_r = ay_1^{r+1} + by_2^{r+1}$, where y_1 and y_2 are the roots of the equation $(d-1)y^2 - (d-\lambda)y + 1 = 0$, subject to the initial and terminal conditions $g_{-1} = g_0$, $g_R = g_{R+1}$. These conditions say that $a(y_1 - 1) = -b(y_2 - 1)$ and $a(y_1 - 1)y_1^{R+1} = -b(y_2 - 1)y_2^{R+1}$. If $y_1 = 1$ or $y_2 = 1$, then the quadratic relation they satisfy yields $\lambda = 0$, and g is readily seen to be constant. If $y_1, y_2 \neq 1$ then $y_1^{R+1} = y_2^{R+1}$. Since $y_1 y_2 = 1/(d-1)$, we get $y_1 = \xi/\sqrt{d-1}$ and $y_2 = \bar{\xi}/\sqrt{d-1}$, where $\xi^{2(R+1)} = 1$. The relation $d - \lambda = (d-1)(y_1 + y_2)$ yields

$$\lambda = d - 2\sqrt{d-1}\,\mathrm{Re}(\xi).$$

Up to rescaling g, we have $g_r = (y_2 - 1)y_1^{r+1} - (y_1 - 1)y_2^{r+1} = y_1 y_2 (y_1^r - y_2^r) - (y_1^{r+1} - y_2^{r+1})$. Using again the relation $y_1 y_2 = 1/(d-1)$, and rescaling g once again, we reach the formula

$$g_r = (d-1)^{-r/2}\big(\text{Im}(\xi^r) - \sqrt{d-1}\,\text{Im}(\xi^{r+1})\big), \quad r = 0, \dots, R.$$

We note that g is non-zero if and only if $\xi \neq \pm 1$. Thus, the Laplacian eigenvalues admitting radial eigenfunctions are

$$\big\{0, d - 2\sqrt{d-1}\,\text{Re}(\xi) : \xi^{2(R+1)} = 1, \xi \neq \pm 1\big\}.$$

$\square$

The eigenvalues of $T_{d,R}$ that we have found are all simple, and there are certainly other eigenvalues. These are hiding in subtrees. Let us remark, however, that the tree $T_{2,R}$ is the path graph on $R+1$ vertices. In this case, eigenfunctions are automatically radial, so we actually have all the eigenvalues.

Corollary 9.22. Consider the path graph P_n on n nodes. Then the adjacency eigenvalues and the Laplacian eigenvalues are

$$\Big\{2\cos\frac{\pi k}{n+1} : k = 1, \dots, n\Big\}, \qquad \Big\{2 - 2\cos\frac{\pi k}{n} : k = 0, \dots, n-1\Big\}.$$

For our purposes, the main consequence of Lemma 9.21 is that it spells out the largest eigenvalues of $T_{d,R}$. Indeed, thanks to Lemma 9.20, we simply have to pick out the largest eigenvalue from each listing.

Theorem 9.23. The largest eigenvalues of $T_{d,R}$ are

$$\alpha_{\max} = 2\sqrt{d-1}\,\cos\frac{\pi}{R+2}, \qquad \lambda_{\max} = d + 2\sqrt{d-1}\,\cos\frac{\pi}{R+1}.$$

Using this theorem, we can bound the largest eigenvalues of a tree in terms of the maximal degree and the diameter.

Corollary 9.24. The largest eigenvalues of a tree with diameter δ satisfy

$$\alpha_{\max} \leq 2\sqrt{d-1}\,\cos\frac{\pi}{\delta+2}, \qquad \lambda_{\max} \leq d + 2\sqrt{d-1}\,\cos\frac{\pi}{\delta+1}.$$

In particular, $\alpha_{\max} < 2\sqrt{d-1}$ and $\lambda_{\max} < d + 2\sqrt{d-1}$.

Proof. Let X be a tree of maximal degree d and diameter δ. Then X can be viewed as a subtree of $T_{d,\delta}$: pick a path of length δ in X, and then hang X by one of the endpoints. Therefore $\alpha_{\max}(X) \leq \alpha_{\max}(T_{d,\delta})$ and $\lambda_{\max}(X) \leq \lambda_{\max}(T_{d,\delta})$. The desired bounds follow from Theorem 9.23. $\square$

For the tree $\tilde{T}_{d,R}$, we could carry out a spectral analysis as for $T_{d,R}$, but the computations are more cumbersome. We will content ourselves with estimates on the largest eigenvalues, obtained by exploiting the relationship with $T_{d,R}$. Namely, $T_{d,R}$ is a subtree of $\tilde{T}_{d,R}$, and $\tilde{T}_{d,R}$ is a subtree of $T_{d,2R}$. From Theorem 9.23 we also deduce the following.

Corollary 9.25. The largest eigenvalues of $\tilde{T}_{d,R}$ satisfy the bounds

$$2\sqrt{d-1}\,\cos\frac{\pi}{R+2} \leq \alpha_{\max} \leq 2\sqrt{d-1}\,\cos\frac{\pi}{2R+2},$$
$$d+2\sqrt{d-1}\,\cos\frac{\pi}{R+1} \leq \lambda_{\max} \leq d+2\sqrt{d-1}\,\cos\frac{\pi}{2R+1}.$$

The function $x \mapsto \cos(\pi/x)$, for $x \geq 2$, is non-negative and increasing to 1 as $x \to \infty$. Elementary calculus shows that $1 - \cos(\pi/x)$ lies between two numerical multiples of $1/x^2$. In asymptotic notation, $1 - \cos(\pi/x) = \Theta(x^{-2})$. So both $\tilde{T}_{d,R}$ and $T_{d,R}$ satisfy

$$\alpha_{\max} = 2\sqrt{d-1} - 2\sqrt{d-1}\,\Theta(R^{-2}),$$
$$\lambda_{\max} = d + 2\sqrt{d-1} - 2\sqrt{d-1}\,\Theta(R^{-2}).$$

Notes. The inequalities $\alpha_{\max} < 2\sqrt{d-1}$ and $\lambda_{\max} < d+2\sqrt{d-1}$ for a tree of maximal degree d, were first proved by Stevanović (*Bounding the largest eigenvalue of trees in terms of the largest vertex degree*, Linear Algebra Appl. 2003; Zbl 1028.05062) with a different argument. Rojo and Robbiano (*An explicit formula for eigenvalues of Bethe trees and upper bounds on the largest eigenvalue of any tree*, Linear Algebra Appl. 2007; Zbl 1126.05069) have computed all the eigenvalues of the tree $T_{d,R}$.

10

More eigenvalues

In this chapter, we take a broader view of graph spectra. We consider all eigenvalues, not just the extremal ones.

10.1 Eigenvalues of symmetric matrices: Courant–Fischer

The Courant–Fischer minimax formulas provide the main tool for understanding the eigenvalues of real symmetric matrices. The power and the versatility of these formulas will become apparent in subsequent sections.

Let M be a real symmetric $n \times n$ matrix, with eigenvalues

$$\mu_{\min} = \mu_1 \leq \cdots \leq \mu_n = \mu_{\max}.$$

We saw in Theorem 9.1 that the extremal eigenvalues can be described in terms of the Rayleigh ratio

$$R(f) = \frac{\langle Mf, f \rangle}{\langle f, f \rangle}$$

as

$$\mu_{\min} = \min_{f \neq 0} R(f), \qquad \mu_{\max} = \max_{f \neq 0} R(f).$$

Broadly speaking, the minimax formulas describe each eigenvalue μ_k via constrained optimizations of the Rayleigh ratio.

Theorem 10.1 (Courant–Fischer). The following hold:

$$\mu_k = \min_{\dim V = k} \max_{f \in V} R(f) = \max_{\dim W = n-k+1} \min_{f \in W} R(f). \tag{10.1}$$

Furthermore, let $f_1, f_2, \ldots, f_n$ be an orthonormal basis of eigenvectors, let V_k denote the linear span of $f_1, \ldots, f_k$, and let W_{n-k+1} denote the linear span of $f_k, \ldots, f_n$. Then

$$\mu_k = \max_{f \in V_k} R(f) = \min_{f \in W_{n-k+1}} R(f). \tag{10.2}$$

Proof. We start by establishing the 'local' formulas (10.2). If $f \in V_k$ then $f = \sum_{i \leq k} c_i f_i$, so

$$R(f) = \frac{\langle Mf, f \rangle}{\langle f, f \rangle} = \frac{\sum_{i \leq k} \mu_i |c_i|^2}{\sum_{i \leq k} |c_i|^2} \leq \mu_k.$$

If $f \in W_{n-k+1}$ then $f = \sum_{i \geq k} c_i f_i$, so

$$R(f) = \frac{\langle Mf, f \rangle}{\langle f, f \rangle} = \frac{\sum_{i \geq k} \mu_i |c_i|^2}{\sum_{i \geq k} |c_i|^2} \geq \mu_k.$$

We conclude by noting that for the eigenvector f_k, which is both in V_k and in W_{n-k+1}, we have $R(f_k) = \mu_k$.

Next, we establish the 'global' formulas (10.1). We clearly have

$$\mu_k = \max_{f \in V_k} R(f) \geq \min_{\dim V = k} \max_{f \in V} R(f).$$

For the reverse inequality, we need to show that $\mu_k \leq \max_{f \in V} R(f)$ for each subspace V of dimension k. We use the following observation: if two subspaces $V, W \subseteq \mathbb{C}^n$ satisfy $\dim V + \dim W > n$, then V and W share a non-zero vector. Hence a k-dimensional space V and the $(n - k + 1)$-dimensional space W_{n-k+1} share a non-zero vector f_0. We then have

$$\mu_k = \min_{f \in W_{n-k+1}} R(f) \leq R(f_0) \leq \max_{f \in V} R(f),$$

as desired. The second minimax formula is established by a similar argument.   □

The min-max formulas for the intermediate eigenvalues are rather unwieldy, even for adjacency and Laplacian matrices. One refreshing and useful exception is a fairly transparent formula for λ_2, the smallest non-trivial Laplacian eigenvalue. The constant function $\mathbb{1}$ is an eigenfunction for the simple eigenvalue $\lambda_1 = 0$, and the space W_{n-1} from the Courant–Fischer theorem is then the orthogonal complement of the subspace spanned by $\mathbb{1}$. We get:

$$\lambda_2 = \min_{0 \neq f \perp \mathbb{1}} \frac{\langle Lf, f \rangle}{\langle f, f \rangle}$$

$$= \min \left\{ \frac{\sum_{\{u,v\} \in E} |f(u) - f(v)|^2}{\sum_{u \in V} |f(u)|^2} : \sum_{u \in V} f(u) = 0, \ f \neq 0 \right\}. \tag{10.3}$$

Exercise 10.2. Show that a graph which is not complete has $\lambda_2 \leq d$ and $\alpha_2 \geq 0$.

10.2 A bound for the Laplacian eigenvalues

The following result is a bound on the growth of Laplacian eigenvalues, formulated in terms of the maximal degree and the diameter. Two ingredients in the proof are the minimax formulas, and our discussion around the largest eigenvalues of trees (Section 9.7).

Theorem 10.3. For a graph of diameter δ, we have

$$\lambda_{k+1} \leq d - 2\sqrt{d-1} \, \cos \frac{2\pi k}{\delta}$$

for all $1 \leq k \leq \delta/2$.

Proof. We break down the proof into three steps. In the first one, we construct a sample function which is supported on a ball, and whose Laplacian Rayleigh ratio is controlled in terms of the radius. In the second step, we argue that there are $k + 1$ balls which are well separated. In the last step, we consider global functions on the graph defined by taking scaled sample functions on each of the $k + 1$ balls.

Step 1. Let B_R be a ball of radius $R \geq 0$ around a vertex v. We show that there is a non-zero function g supported on B_R such that

$$\frac{\langle Lg, g \rangle}{\langle g, g \rangle} \leq d - 2\sqrt{d-1} \, \cos \frac{\pi}{R+2}. \tag{$*$}$$

If $R = 0$, take g to be 1 at v and 0 elsewhere. Then the left-hand side of $(*)$ is $\deg(v)$ while the right-hand side is d.

Assume $R \geq 1$. Consider the tree $\tilde{T}_{d,R}$, and let α_T denote its largest adjacency eigenvalue. Let f be a positive eigenfunction on $\tilde{T}_{d,R}$ for α_T. Since f is radial, we may view it as a function of the radius $r \mapsto f_r$, for $r = 0, \ldots, R$. Spelling out the eigenrelation for f, we get

$$\alpha_T f_0 = df_1, \quad \alpha_T f_r = f_{r-1} + (d-1)f_{r+1} \quad \text{for } r = 1, \ldots, R,$$

with the convention that $f_{R+1} = 0$. These relations, and the fact that $\alpha_T < d$, imply that f is decreasing. Indeed, the first relation yields $f_0 > f_1$, while the second relation yields that $f_r > f_{r+1}$ provided $f_{r-1} > f_r$.

Next, we define a function g by transplanting f onto the ball B_R. Namely, foliate B_R into spheres S_r for $r = 0, \ldots, R$, and set $g \equiv f_r$ on S_r. Also set $g \equiv 0$ outside B_R. We claim that the pointwise bound

$$Lg \leq (d - \alpha_T)g$$

holds on B_R. Indeed, let $u \in S_r$. We argue the generic case $r > 0$, leaving the case $r = 0$ (i.e., $u = v$) to the reader. As u has at least one neighbour on S_{r-1}, and f is decreasing in r, we have

$$Ag(u) \geq f_{r-1} + (\deg(u) - 1)f_{r+1} = \alpha_T f_r - (d - \deg(u))f_{r+1}$$
$$\geq \alpha_T f_r - (d - \deg(u))f_r = (\alpha_T - d + \deg(u))g(u).$$

Hence

$$Lg(u) = \deg(u)g(u) - Ag(u) \le (d - \alpha_T)g(u),$$

as claimed. As g is positive on B_R and vanishes off B_R, the pointwise bound yields $\langle Lg, g \rangle \le (d - \alpha_T)\langle g, g \rangle$. Now $(*)$ follows, by using the lower bound on α_T from Corollary 9.25.

Step 2. Let $R = \left\lfloor \frac{1}{2k}\delta \right\rfloor - 1$, and note that $R \ge 0$. We show that there are $k + 1$ balls of radius R in X, $B_R(v_i)$ for $i = 1, \ldots, k + 1$, which are completely separated: they are disjoint, and there are no edges between them.

Indeed, let v_1 and v_{k+1} be vertices with $\mathrm{dist}(v_1, v_{k+1}) = \delta$, and pick a path of length δ between them. As $2(R + 1) \le \frac{1}{k}\delta$, we may successively pick vertices $v_2, \ldots, v_k$ on the path such that the distance between two consecutive vertices is at least $2(R + 1)$. In fact, the distance between any two distinct vertices is at least $2(R + 1)$. It follows that any two balls $B_R(v_i)$ and $B_R(v_j)$, where $i \ne j$, are completely separated: if $p_i \in B_R(v_i)$ and $p_j \in B_R(v_j)$ then $2(R + 1) \le \mathrm{dist}(v_i, v_j) \le 2R + \mathrm{dist}(p_i, p_j)$ so $\mathrm{dist}(p_i, p_j) \ge 2$.

Step 3. For each ball $B_R(v_i)$, let g_i be a function supported on $B_R(v_i)$ as in step 1. Then $g_1, \ldots, g_{k+1}$ are mutually orthogonal since the balls $B_R(v_1), \ldots, B_R(v_{k+1})$ are completely separated. Furthermore, Lg_i is supported on $B_{R+1}(v_i)$, hence orthogonal to g_j for each $j \ne i$. For a non-zero linear combination $\phi = \sum c_i g_i$ we have

$$\langle L\phi, \phi \rangle = \sum |c_i|^2 \langle Lg_i, g_i \rangle, \qquad \langle \phi, \phi \rangle = \sum |c_i|^2 \langle g_i, g_i \rangle,$$

so

$$\frac{\langle L\phi, \phi \rangle}{\langle \phi, \phi \rangle} \le d - 2\sqrt{d - 1}\, \cos \frac{\pi}{R + 2} \le d - 2\sqrt{d - 1}\, \cos \frac{2\pi k}{\delta},$$

as $R + 2 = \left\lfloor \frac{1}{2k}\delta \right\rfloor + 1 > \frac{1}{2k}\delta$. On the other hand, by the minimax formulas we have

$$\lambda_{k+1} \le \max_{0 \ne \phi \in V} \frac{\langle L\phi, \phi \rangle}{\langle \phi, \phi \rangle}$$

for the $(k + 1)$-dimensional space V spanned by $g_1, \ldots, g_{k+1}$. We conclude the proof by combining the last two inequalities.   □

For regular graphs, we immediately deduce a quantitative bound on the adjacency eigenvalues:

Corollary 10.4. For a d-regular graph with diameter δ, we have

$$\alpha_{k+1} \ge 2\sqrt{d - 1}\, \cos \frac{2\pi k}{\delta}$$

for all $1 \le k \le \delta/2$.

This has, in turn, an interesting qualitative consequence. The diameter of a d-regular graph tends to infinity as the size grows to infinity, and then the above lower bound tends to $2\sqrt{d-1}$. We obtain the following corollary:

Corollary 10.5. Fix a threshold $t < 2\sqrt{d-1}$. Then $\alpha_2 > t$ for all but finitely many d-regular graphs. More generally, for each $k \geq 2$ we have $\alpha_k > t$ for all but finitely many d-regular graphs.

Notes. Naturally, it all happened backwards. First came the last corollary. The part concerning α_2 is stated in a paper of Alon (*Eigenvalues and expanders*, Combinatorica 1986; Zbl 0661.05053) as a result due Alon and Boppana. Lubotzky, Phillips, and Sarnak (*Ramanujan graphs*, Combinatorica 1988; Zbl 0661.05035) proved a weak version of the Alon–Boppana result. The first published proof, and a quantitative one, of the Alon–Boppana result was subsequently given by Alon's alter ego Nilli (*On the second eigenvalue of a graph*, Discrete Math. 1991; Zbl 0771.05064). Meanwhile, Burger established the general version in unpublished work (*Cheng's inequality for graphs*, preprint 1987). It has been pointed out by Friedman that the Alon–Boppana phenomenon — namely, escape of eigenvalues towards $2\sqrt{d-1}$ and beyond — is implicit in work of McKay (*The expected eigenvalue distribution of a large regular graph*, Linear Algebra Appl. 1981; Zbl 0468.05039).

Corollary 10.4 came after. The earliest reference is Friedman (*Some geometric aspects of graphs and their eigenfunctions*, Duke Math. J. 1993; Zbl 0785.05066), followed by Quenell (*Eigenvalue comparisons in graph theory*, Pacific J. Math. 1996; Zbl 0877.05036) with an independent account. See also Nilli (*Tight estimates for eigenvalues of regular graphs*, Electron. J. Combin. 2004; Zbl 1053.05082) for a short argument. With some hindsight, the corollary can already be glimpsed in a paper by Brooks (*The spectral geometry of k-regular groups*, J. Anal. Math. 1991; Zbl 0772.58061).

Theorem 10.3 is essentially due to Urakawa (*Eigenvalue comparison theorems of the discrete Laplacians for a graph*, Geom. Dedicata 1999; Zbl 0921.58067). Our approach is somewhat different, and somewhat simpler. Theorem 10.3 is the graph-theoretic analogue of a bound due to Cheng (*Eigenvalue comparison theorems and its geometric applications*, Math. Z. 1975; Zbl 0329.53035) for the Laplacian eigenvalues on a compact Riemannian manifold.

10.3 Eigenvalues of symmetric matrices: Cauchy and Weyl

We now turn to the behaviour of eigenvalues with respect to several operations on symmetric matrices. We discuss two general principles, Cauchy's interlacing theorem and Weyl's inequality. The first one addresses the operation of deleting a row and the corresponding column. The second one concerns addition. Both results are applications of the Courant–Fischer minimax formulas.

Theorem 10.6 (Cauchy). Let M be a symmetric $n \times n$ matrix, and let M' be the symmetric $(n-1) \times (n-1)$ matrix obtained by deleting the first row and the first column of M. Then the eigenvalues of M' interlace the eigenvalues of M:

$$\mu_1 \le \mu_1' \le \mu_2 \le \cdots \le \mu_{n-1} \le \mu_{n-1}' \le \mu_n.$$

Proof. Let ϕ denote the linear embedding $\mathbb{C}^{n-1} \hookrightarrow \mathbb{C}^n$ given by adding 0 as a first coordinate. Then the Rayleigh ratios of M' and M are related by the formula $R'(f') = R(\phi(f'))$.

We have to show that $\mu_k \le \mu_k' \le \mu_{k+1}$ for $k = 1, \ldots, n-1$. Now

$$\mu_k' = \min_{\dim V'=k} \max_{f' \in V'} R'(f')$$

$$= \min_{\dim V'=k} \max_{f \in \phi(V')} R(f) \ge \min_{\dim V=k} \max_{f \in V} R(f) = \mu_k$$

and

$$\mu_k' = \max_{\dim W'=n-k} \min_{f' \in W'} R'(f')$$

$$= \max_{\dim W'=n-k} \min_{f \in \phi(W')} R(f) \le \max_{\dim W=n-k} \min_{f \in W} R(f) = \mu_{k+1},$$

as desired. $\qquad\qquad\qquad\qquad\qquad\qquad\qquad\qquad\qquad\qquad\qquad\qquad\qquad\quad$ □

Theorem 10.7 (Weyl). Let M and N be symmetric $n \times n$ matrices. Then

$$\mu_{k+\ell-1}(M+N) \ge \mu_k(M) + \mu_\ell(N)$$

as long as the indices satisfy $1 \le k, \ell, k + \ell - 1 \le n$.

Proof. If three subspaces $U, V, W \subseteq \mathbb{C}^n$ satisfy $\dim U + \dim V + \dim W > 2n$, then U, V and W share a non-zero vector. The three subspaces we will use are: the subspace W_{n-k+1} with respect to M, the subspace $W_{n-\ell+1}$ with respect to N, and the subspace $V_{k+\ell-1}$ with respect to $M+N$. For a common non-zero vector f_0, we have

$$\mu_{k+\ell-1}(M+N) \ge R_{M+N}(f_0) = R_M(f_0) + R_N(f_0) \ge \mu_k(M) + \mu_\ell(N),$$

as claimed. $\qquad\qquad\qquad\qquad\qquad\qquad\qquad\qquad\qquad\qquad\qquad\qquad\qquad\quad$ □

Weyl's inequality provides lower and upper bounds for the eigenvalues of $M+N$, thought of as a perturbation of M by N. Let us single out the simplest bounds of this kind.

Corollary 10.8. Let M and N be symmetric $n \times n$ matrices. Then

$$\mu_k(M) + \mu_{\min}(N) \le \mu_k(M + N) \le \mu_k(M) + \mu_{\max}(N). \tag{10.4}$$

Proof. The lower bound $\mu_k(M) + \mu_{\min}(N) \le \mu_k(M + N)$ is the case $\ell = 1$ of Weyl's inequality. Replacing M by $M + N$, and N by $-N$, we get $\mu_k(M + N) + \mu_{\min}(-N) \le \mu_k(M)$. As $\mu_{\min}(-N) = -\mu_{\max}(N)$, this is precisely the upper bound $\mu_k(M + N) \le \mu_k(M) + \mu_{\max}(N)$. □

Here is a simple application of the previous corollary to graph eigenvalues. Recall that, for a d-regular graph, the adjacency and the Laplacian eigenvalues are related by $\alpha_k + \lambda_k = d$. In general, $\alpha_k + \lambda_k$ is confined to the interval determined by the minimal and the maximal vertex degrees.

Proposition 10.9. The adjacency and the Laplacian eigenvalues of a graph satisfy

$$d_{\min} \le \alpha_k + \lambda_k \le d.$$

Proof. Apply the inequality (10.4) to $M = -A$, and $N = \text{diag}(\deg)$, the diagonal matrix recording the degrees. Thus $M + N = L$. The relevant eigenvalues are $\mu_k(M) = -\alpha_k$, $\mu_k(M + N) = \lambda_k$, and $\mu_{\min}(N) = d_{\min}$, $\mu_{\max}(N) = d$. Thus $-\alpha_k + d_{\min} \le \lambda_k \le -\alpha_k + d$, as desired. □

Exercise 10.10. Let M be a symmetric matrix of size n, partitioned as

$$M = \begin{pmatrix} M' & N \\ N^t & M'' \end{pmatrix},$$

where M' and M'' are symmetric matrices of size n', respectively n''. Show that $\mu_1 + \mu_{k+\ell} \le \mu'_k + \mu''_\ell$ for $1 \le k \le n'$, $1 \le \ell \le n''$.

Notes. Proposition 10.9 is an observation of Nikiforov (*Eigenvalues and extremal degrees of graphs*, Linear Algebra Appl. 2006; Zbl 1114.05062). Exercise 10.10 is a finite-dimensional instance of a result due to Aronszajn (*Rayleigh-Ritz and A. Weinstein methods for approximation of eigenvalues I. Operators in a Hilbert space*, Proc. Nat. Acad. Sci. USA 1948; Zbl 0031.40601).

10.4 Subgraphs

How do the eigenvalues of a graph change upon passing to a subgraph? For the largest adjacency or Laplacian eigenvalues, we addressed this question in Theorem 9.17. We can now extend our scope to the entire spectrum, thanks to the Cauchy and Weyl inequalities. In this section, we dispense with the usual connectivity assumption. We maintain, however, the non-degeneracy assumption that $n \geq 3$.

Starting with an ambient graph, one gets a subgraph by two operations: removing vertices and removing edges. We will take a close look at each one, proving in particular the following:

Theorem 10.11. If X' is a spanning subgraph of X, then the Laplacian eigenvalues satisfy $\lambda'_k \leq \lambda_k$. If X' is an induced subgraph of X, then the adjacency eigenvalues satisfy $\alpha'_k \leq \alpha_k$.

A spanning subgraph is a subgraph having all the vertices of the ambient graph. An induced subgraph is a subgraph having all the edges inherited from the ambient graph. The above theorem conforms with the philosophy that Laplacian eigenvalues sense the edges, while adjacency eigenvalues sense the vertices.

Example 10.12. A graph is said to be *hamiltonian* if it contains a spanning cycle, meaning a cycle that visits every vertex. Graphically, this means that the graph can be drawn as a cycle with additional chords.

The Petersen graph is not hamiltonian. This can be argued combinatorially, but a spectral proof fits the discussion. Let us assume that the Petersen graph has a hamiltonian cycle. This means that the cycle C_{10} is a spanning subgraph of the Petersen graph, and so $\lambda_k(C_{10}) \leq \lambda_k(\text{Pet})$ for all $k = 1, \ldots, 10$. Listing the Laplacian eigenvalues of C_{10} and those of the Petersen graph, we find that the inequality fails for $k = 6$.

k	1	2	3	4	5	6	7	8	9	10
$\lambda_k(C_{10})$	0	0.4...	0.4...	1.4...	1.4...	2.6...	2.6...	3.6...	3.6...	4
$\lambda_k(\text{Pet})$	0	2	2	2	2	2	5	5	5	5

The next two theorems give bounds for both the adjacency and the Laplacian eigenvalues, when either a vertex or an edge is removed from the ambient graph.

Theorem 10.13. Let X' be a graph obtained by removing a vertex from the graph X. Then the adjacency and the Laplacian eigenvalues of X' can be bounded as

$$\alpha_{k+1} \leq \alpha'_k \leq \alpha_k, \tag{10.5}$$
$$\lambda_k - 1 \leq \lambda'_k \leq \lambda_{k+1}. \tag{10.6}$$

Proof. Label the vertices $1, 2, \ldots, n$ so that the removed vertex is 1. The adjacency matrix A' is obtained by deleting the first row and column of the adjacency matrix A. Cauchy's interlacing theorem is directly applicable, yielding (10.5).

The Laplacian matrix L' is given by $L' = M + N$, where M denotes the matrix obtained by deleting the first row and column of the Laplacian matrix L, and N is

$$\begin{pmatrix} -I_{\deg(1)} & \\ & 0_{n-1-\deg(1)} \end{pmatrix}.$$

Here $\deg(1)$ denotes, as usual, the degree of vertex 1, and we furthermore assume that the neighbours of 1 come right after (2, 3, and so on). The smallest eigenvalue of N is -1. The largest is 0, except when $\deg(1) = n - 1$ in which case it is -1. By (10.4), we have $\mu_k(M) - 1 \le \lambda'_k \le \mu_k(M)$ for $k = 1, \ldots, n - 1$. On the other hand, Cauchy's interlacing theorem says that $\lambda_k \le \mu_k(M) \le \lambda_{k+1}$ for $k = 1, \ldots, n-1$. The two-sided bounds (10.6) follow. $\square$

Theorem 10.14. Let X' be a graph obtained by removing an edge from the graph X. Then the adjacency and the Laplacian eigenvalues of X' can be bounded as

$$\alpha_k - 1 \le \alpha'_k \le \alpha_k + 1, \tag{10.7}$$
$$\lambda_k - 2 \le \lambda'_k \le \lambda_k. \tag{10.8}$$

Proof. Label the vertices $1, 2, \ldots, n$ so that the removed edge is the one between 1 and 2. The adjacency matrix of X' and that of X are related by $A' = A + N$, where A is the adjacency matrix of X, and N is

$$\begin{pmatrix} 0 & -1 & \\ -1 & 0 & \\ & & 0_{n-2} \end{pmatrix}.$$

This matrix has simple eigenvalues ± 1, as well as 0 with multiplicity $n - 2$. The bound (10.4), with $n - k$ in place of k, yields (10.7).

The Laplacian matrix of X' and that of X are related by $L' = L + N$, where N is

$$\begin{pmatrix} -1 & 1 & \\ 1 & -1 & \\ & & 0_{n-2} \end{pmatrix}.$$

The eigenvalues of this matrix are -2 with multiplicity 1, and 0 with multiplicity $n - 1$. Now (10.4) gives (10.8). $\square$

Revisiting the proof, we see that the adjacency part of the edge-removal theorem can be generalized.

Theorem 10.15. Let Y be a subgraph of X, and let X' be the graph obtained from X by removing the edges of Y. Then the adjacency eigenvalues of X' satisfy the bounds

$$\alpha_k - \alpha_{\max}(Y) \le \alpha'_k \le \alpha_k - \alpha_{\min}(Y). \tag{10.9}$$

Exercise 10.16. Show that a tree of diameter δ has

$$\lambda_2 \leq 2 - 2\cos\frac{\pi}{\delta + 1}.$$

Deduce that $\lambda_2 \leq 1$, with equality if and only if the tree is a star graph.

Notes. A spectral proof of the fact that the Petersen graph is not hamiltonian was first given by Mohar (*A domain monotonicity theorem for graphs and Hamiltonicity*, Discrete Appl. Math. 1992; Zbl 0765.05071). A simpler argument, essentially the one explained in Example 10.12, was noticed by van den Heuvel (*Hamilton cycles and eigenvalues of graphs*, Linear Algebra Appl. 1995; Zbl 0846.05059).

The result of Exercise 10.16 is due to Grone, Merris, and Sunder (*The Laplacian spectrum of a graph*, SIAM J. Matrix Anal. Appl. 1990; Zbl 0733.05060).

11

Spectral bounds

The focus of this chapter is on bounds relating graph eigenvalues to graph invariants and other combinatorial properties.

11.1 Chromatic number and independence number

We start with one of the earliest results in spectral graph theory. It gives a spectral improvement of the upper bound $\mathrm{chr} \leq 1 + d$.

Theorem 11.1 (Wilf). The chromatic number of a graph X satisfies $\mathrm{chr}\, X \leq 1 + \alpha_{\max}$.

Proof. We argue as in the proof of Proposition 2.2, inducting on the size. Let X' be the (possibly disconnected) graph obtained by removing a vertex v of minimal degree. The induction hypothesis, and the inequality $\alpha'_{\max} \leq \alpha_{\max}$, imply that X' can be coloured using at most $1 + \alpha_{\max}$ colours. Since $\deg(v) \leq d_{\mathrm{ave}} \leq \alpha_{\max}$, there is at least one more colour available to complete the colouring. □

One may wonder whether the better bound $\mathrm{chr} \leq 1 + d_{\mathrm{ave}}$ holds. The above proof does not work since d_{ave}, unlike d and $\alpha_{\max}$, may increase by passing to subgraphs. And a counterexample is not hard to find: the graph obtained from K_n by attaching a pendant edge at each vertex has $\mathrm{chr} = n$ and $d_{\mathrm{ave}} = \frac{1}{2}(n + 1)$.

The next result gives a lower bound for the chromatic number in terms of adjacency eigenvalues. Recall that non-trivial graphs have $\alpha_{\min} < 0$.

Theorem 11.2 (Hoffman). The chromatic number of a graph X satisfies

$$\mathrm{chr}\, X \geq 1 + \frac{\alpha_{\max}}{-\alpha_{\min}}.$$

Proof. Let f be a positive eigenfunction for $\alpha_{\max}$. Given an independent set of vertices, S, we consider the perturbation $f_S = f + af \cdot \mathbb{1}_S$, where $\mathbb{1}_S$ is the characteristic function of S, and $a \in \mathbb{R}$ will be chosen later. On the one hand, we have

$$\langle f_S, f_S \rangle = \langle f, f \rangle + 2a\langle f, f \cdot \mathbb{1}_S \rangle + a^2 \langle f \cdot \mathbb{1}_S, f \cdot \mathbb{1}_S \rangle$$
$$= \langle f, f \rangle + (a^2 + 2a)\langle f, f \cdot \mathbb{1}_S \rangle.$$

On the other hand,

$$\langle A f_S, f_S \rangle = \langle A f, f \rangle + 2a \langle A f, f \cdot 1_S \rangle + a^2 \langle A(f \cdot 1_S), f \cdot 1_S \rangle$$
$$= \langle A f, f \rangle + 2a \langle A f, f \cdot 1_S \rangle$$

by using the symmetry of A, and the independence of S.

Now let χ denote the chromatic number, and consider a chromatic partition of the vertex set into χ independent subsets $S_1, \ldots, S_\chi$. For each S_k, let f_k be the corresponding perturbation of f. Adding up the previous relations, we get

$$\sum \langle f_k, f_k \rangle = (\chi + a^2 + 2a) \langle f, f \rangle,$$
$$\sum \langle A f_k, f_k \rangle = (\chi + 2a) \langle A f, f \rangle = (\chi + 2a) \alpha_{\max} \langle f, f \rangle.$$

As $\langle A f_k, f_k \rangle \geq \alpha_{\min} \langle f_k, f_k \rangle$ for each k, we are led to the inequality

$$(\chi + 2a) \alpha_{\max} \geq (\chi + a^2 + 2a) \alpha_{\min}.$$

Now taking $a = -\chi$, we obtain $\alpha_{\max} \leq -(\chi - 1)\alpha_{\min}$. This is the desired inequality.
$\square$

Exercise 11.3. Give an alternate proof of the previous theorem by using the result of Exercise 10.10.

We now turn to the independence number, where we get an upper bound in Laplacian terms.

Theorem 11.4 (Hoffman). The independence number of a graph X on n vertices satisfies

$$\operatorname{ind} X \leq n \left(1 - \frac{d_{\min}}{\lambda_{\max}} \right).$$

Proof. Let S be a proper subset of vertices, and consider the function f defined by $f \equiv |S^c|$ on S, respectively $f \equiv -|S|$ on S^c. We compute

$$\langle f, f \rangle = \sum_{u \in S} f(u)^2 + \sum_{u \in S^c} f(u)^2 = |S| \cdot |S^c|^2 + |S^c| \cdot |S|^2 = n |S| \, |S^c|,$$
$$\langle L f, f \rangle = \sum_{\{u,v\} \in E} |f(u) - f(v)|^2 = \sum_{\{u,v\} \in \partial S} |f(u) - f(v)|^2 = n^2 |\partial S|,$$

and so

$$\frac{\langle L f, f \rangle}{\langle f, f \rangle} = \frac{n |\partial S|}{|S| \, |S^c|}. \tag{11.1}$$

Now, if S is an independent subset, then all edges emanating from vertices of S are in ∂S, so $|\partial S| \geq d_{min}|S|$. The Rayleigh ratio on the left-hand side of (11.1) is at most λ_{max}. Therefore

$$\lambda_{max} \geq \frac{nd_{min}}{n - |S|},$$

that is, $|S| \leq n(1 - d_{min}/\lambda_{max})$. The claim follows.   □

In practice, the previous two theorems are often applied to regular graphs. In this case, they can be stated as follows.

Corollary 11.5. For a regular graph X, we have

$$\text{ind } X \leq \frac{n}{1 - d/\alpha_{min}}, \qquad \text{chr } X \geq 1 - d/\alpha_{min}.$$

For the independence number, we have rewritten the bound of Theorem 11.4 by using the relation $\alpha_{min} + \lambda_{max} = d$. A practical motivation is that computations usually provide the adjacency eigenvalues. For the chromatic number, we have used $\alpha_{max} = d$ in the bound provided by Theorem 11.2.

In the regular case, the chromatic bound can be derived from the independence bound by using the inequality $\text{chr } X \cdot \text{ind } X \geq n$. For a general graph X, the independence bound of Theorem 11.4 and the inequality $\text{chr } X \cdot \text{ind } X \geq n$ imply the chromatic bound

$$\text{chr } X \geq \frac{1}{1 - d_{min}/\lambda_{max}}.$$

Note, however, that this is no better than the adjacency bound of Theorem 11.2. For $\alpha_{max} \geq d_{ave} \geq d_{min}$ and $\alpha_{min} + \lambda_{max} \geq d_{min}$, we get

$$1 + \frac{\alpha_{max}}{-\alpha_{min}} \geq 1 + \frac{d_{min}}{\lambda_{max} - d_{min}} = \frac{1}{1 - d_{min}/\lambda_{max}}.$$

Example 11.6. Consider the Paley graph $P(q)$, where $q \equiv 1 \bmod 4$. Plugging in $n = q$, $d = \frac{1}{2}(q - 1)$, and $\alpha_{min} = -\frac{1}{2}(\sqrt{q} + 1)$ in the previous corollary, we find that

$$\text{ind } P(q) \leq \sqrt{q} \leq \text{chr } P(q).$$

These are fairly good bounds. As we saw in Proposition 5.12, equalities hold when q is a square.

Notes. Theorem 11.1 is due to Wilf (*The eigenvalues of a graph and its chromatic number*, J. London Math. Soc. 1967; Zbl 0144.45202). Theorem 11.2 is due to Hoffman (*On eigenvalues and colorings of graphs*, in 'Graph theory and its applications', Academic Press 1970; Zbl 0221.05061) but the proof given above is based on an argument of Nikiforov (*Chromatic number and spectral radius*, Linear Algebra Appl. 2007; Zbl 1125.05063). Hoffman's original approach is that of Exercise 11.3. Theorem 11.4 is also due to Hoffman (unpublished).

11.2 Isoperimetric constant

The smallest positive eigenvalue of the Laplacian, λ_2, is an indicator of how well a graph is connected. This principle arises from, and is made quantitative by, relations between λ_2 and various graph-theoretic measures of connectivity. Here we pursue the relation with the isoperimetric constant. As we will see, the spectral perspective on the isoperimetric constant turns out to be particularly successful. It is, in fact, one of the most consistent and conceptual instances of understanding combinatorial aspects by spectral methods.

We start with a spectral lower bound on the isoperimetric constant.

Theorem 11.7 (Alon–Milman). A graph X has iso $X \geq \lambda_2/2$.

Proof. Recall (11.1):

$$\frac{\langle Lf, f \rangle}{\langle f, f \rangle} = \frac{n|\partial S|}{|S||S^c|},$$

where S is a proper subset of vertices, and f is the function given by $f \equiv |S^c|$ on S, respectively $f \equiv -|S|$ on S^c. As $f \perp \mathbb{1}$, the left-hand side is at least λ_2. So, if S is such that $|S| \leq n/2$, then

$$\lambda_2 \leq \frac{n|\partial S|}{|S||S^c|} \leq 2\frac{|\partial S|}{|S|},$$

implying that iso $X \geq \lambda_2/2$. $\square$

There is an upper bound of a similar flavour. This bound, however, requires additional spectral information.

Theorem 11.8. If a graph X has a Laplacian eigenvalue λ with a $\{\pm 1\}$-valued eigenfunction, then iso $X \leq \lambda/2$.

Proof. Let g be a $\{\pm 1\}$-valued eigenfunction for λ, and let $S = \{v : g(v) = 1\}$. As g is orthogonal to $\mathbb{1}$, we have $|S| = n/2$. Now $\langle Lg, g \rangle = 4|\partial S|$ and $\langle g, g \rangle = n = 2|S|$. Therefore

$$\lambda = \frac{\langle Lg, g \rangle}{\langle g, g \rangle} = 2\frac{|\partial S|}{|S|} \geq 2 \text{ iso } X,$$

as claimed. $\square$

Note that, if λ is to have a $\{\pm 1\}$-valued eigenfunction g, then λ has to be an even integer. Indeed, in the eigenrelation $\lambda g(v) = \deg(v)g(v) - \sum_{u:u \sim v} g(u)$, the right-hand side is an even integer. Also, n has to be even since g is orthogonal to $\mathbb{1}$.

An immediate consequence of the previous two theorems is the following.

Corollary 11.9. If a graph X has the property that λ_2 admits a $\{\pm 1\}$-valued eigenfunction, then iso $X = \lambda_2/2$.

This criterion for computing the isoperimetric constant is applicable in many examples. For some of them, we have already found the isoperimetric constant by combinatorial arguments. But even in these cases, the spectral approach is more satisfactory. One context where we know not only the eigenvalues, but also corresponding eigenfunctions, is that of Cayley graphs and bi-Cayley graphs of abelian groups. Some of the examples that follow will exploit that perspective.

Example 11.10. The Petersen graph has $\lambda_2 = 2$. A corresponding $\{\pm 1\}$-valued eigenfunction is most easily seen on the standard drawing of the Petersen graph. Put $+1$ on the vertices of the outer pentagon, and -1 on the vertices of the inner pentagram. It follows that the isoperimetric constant equals 1.

Example 11.11. The cube graph Q_n has $\lambda_2 = 2$. Putting $+1$ on binary strings starting in 0, respectively -1 on binary strings starting in 1, defines a $\{\pm 1\}$-valued eigenfunction for λ_2. Hence iso $Q_n = 1$.

In fact, for *any* Cayley graph of $(\mathbb{Z}_2)^n$ we can find a $\{\pm 1\}$-valued eigenfunction for λ_2. The reason is that λ_2 admits some non-trivial character as an eigenfunction, and all non-trivial characters of $(\mathbb{Z}_2)^n$ are $\{\pm 1\}$-valued. So the isoperimetric constant equals $\lambda_2/2$, an integer, for any Cayley graph of $(\mathbb{Z}_2)^n$.

Exercise 11.12. (i) Show that the halved cube graph $\frac{1}{2}Q_n$ has isoperimetric constant $n - 1$. (ii) For a fixed n, consider the decked cube graphs $DQ_n(a)$ for varying $a \in (\mathbb{Z}_2)^n$. Which choice of a maximizes the isoperimetric constant of $DQ_n(a)$?

Example 11.13. Consider the twin graphs, $K_4 \times K_4$ and the Shrikhande graph. Both have $\lambda_2 = 4$, and for both graphs we can find a corresponding $\{\pm 1\}$-valued eigenfunction. Referring to Figure 3.1, the eigenfunctions are defined as follows. In $K_4 \times K_4$, we alternatively put $+1$ and -1 as we circle around the vertex set. In the Shrikhande graph, we put $+1$ on the vertices of the outer octagon, and -1 on all the inner vertices. So, in both cases, the isoperimetric constant is 2.

Our seemingly lucky choice of eigenfunctions prompts a legitimate concern: what if the Cheshire Cat takes away our nice picture of, say, the Shrikhande graph? We are then left with a Cayley graph description, inviting us to take an algebraic approach. And we find that, as in the previous example, more is true: *any* Cayley graph of $(\mathbb{Z}_4)^n$ admits a $\{\pm 1\}$-valued eigenfunction for λ_2. Indeed, λ_2 has a non-trivial character χ as an eigenfunction. Now χ takes values in $\{\pm 1, \pm i\}$. The real and imaginary parts of χ, $\text{Re}(\chi)$ and $\text{Im}(\chi)$, are eigenfunctions for λ_2. So $\text{Re}(\chi) + \text{Im}(\chi)$, which is $\{\pm 1\}$-valued, is an eigenfunction as well. We conclude that any Cayley graph of $(\mathbb{Z}_4)^n$ has isoperimetric constant $\lambda_2/2$.

Example 11.14. For the incidence graph $I_n(q)$, we know that

$$\lambda_2 = d - \alpha_2 = \frac{q^{n-1} - 1}{q - 1} - q^{n/2-1}.$$

Our aim is to show that, for suitable q and n, the lower bound iso $I_n(q) \geq \lambda_2/2$ becomes an equality.

Let us think of $I_n(q)$ as the bi-Cayley graph of $\mathbb{K}^*/\mathbb{F}^*$ with respect to $\{[s] : \mathrm{Tr}(s) = 0\}$. Assuming that q is odd, a $\{\pm 1\}$-valued multiplicative character of $\mathbb{K}$ — in fact, the only one — is the quadratic character σ. If we also assume that n is even, then σ is trivial on $\mathbb{F}^*$ so it defines a $\{\pm 1\}$-valued character, still denoted σ, of $\mathbb{K}^*/\mathbb{F}^*$. We now refer to the arguments of Theorem 8.8 and Example 8.10. As α_σ is real, in fact integral, we have that the adjacency eigenvalue $|\alpha_\sigma| = \pm \alpha_\sigma$ has an eigenfunction given by σ on the black vertices and $\pm \sigma$ on the white vertices. In other words, the second largest eigenvalue $\alpha_2 = q^{n/2} - 1$ has a $\{\pm 1\}$-valued eigenfunction. We conclude that, for q odd and n even, the incidence graph $I_n(q)$ has isoperimetric constant $\lambda_2/2$. As a concrete example, iso $I_4(q) = \frac{1}{2}(q^2 + 1)$.

The next result is a rather different spectral upper bound for the isoperimetric constant.

Theorem 11.15 (Dodziuk). *A graph X with maximal degree d satisfies iso $X \leq \sqrt{2d\lambda_2}$.*

Proof. We proceed in three steps. The first step is a functional inequality involving the isoperimetric constant, herein denoted β. The second step turns the ℓ^1 inequality of the first step into an ℓ^2 inequality. In the third step, we apply the inequality established in the second step to the positive part of an eigenfunction for λ_2.

Step 1. Let f be a non-negative function on the graph, supported on no more than half the vertices. Then

$$\beta \sum_v f(v) \leq \sum_{\{u,v\} \in E} |f(u) - f(v)|.$$

Indeed, let $0 = f_0 < f_1 < \cdots < f_s$ be the values taken by f. We write

$$\sum_{\{u,v\} \in E} |f(u) - f(v)| = \sum_{k \geq 1} N_k f_k.$$

The coefficients are given by

$$N_k = E(\{f = f_k\}, \{f < f_k\}) - E(\{f = f_k\}, \{f > f_k\}),$$

where, say, $E(\{f = f_k\}, \{f > f_k\})$ denotes the number of edges between the vertex subsets $\{v : f(v) = f_k\}$ and $\{v : f(v) > f_k\}$. We then have

$$N_k = E(\{f \geq f_k\}, \{f < f_k\}) - E(\{f \leq f_k\}, \{f > f_k\})$$
$$= |\partial \{f \geq f_k\}| - |\partial \{f \geq f_{k+1}\}|.$$

Put $S_k = \{f \geq f_k\}$. Then

$$\sum_{k\geq 1} N_k f_k = \sum_{k\geq 1} \left(|\partial S_k| - |\partial S_{k+1}|\right) f_k = \sum_{k\geq 1} |\partial S_k|(f_k - f_{k-1}).$$

At this point, we can bring in β. For each $k \geq 1$, the set S_k contains no more than half the vertices, so $|\partial S_k| \geq \beta |S_k|$. Therefore

$$\sum_{k\geq 1} N_k f_k \geq \beta \sum_{k\geq 1} |S_k|(f_k - f_{k-1}) = \beta \sum_{k\geq 1} \left(|S_k| - |S_{k+1}|\right) f_k$$

$$= \beta \sum_{k\geq 1} |\{f = f_k\}| f_k = \beta \sum_v f(v),$$

as claimed.

Step 2. Let f be a real-valued function, supported on no more than half the vertices. Then

$$\beta^2 \langle f, f \rangle \leq 2d \langle Lf, f \rangle.$$

Indeed, the bound from step 1, applied to f^2, says that

$$\beta \sum_v f(v)^2 \leq \sum_{\{u,v\}\in E} \left|f^2(u) - f^2(v)\right|.$$

Now $|f^2(u) - f^2(v)| = |f(u) - f(v)| \cdot |f(u) + f(v)|$ and so, by Cauchy–Schwarz, we have

$$\left(\sum_{\{u,v\}\in E} \left|f^2(u) - f^2(v)\right| \right)^2 \leq \left(\sum_{\{u,v\}\in E} |f(u) - f(v)|^2 \right)\left(\sum_{\{u,v\}\in E} |f(u) + f(v)|^2 \right).$$

The first factor on the right-hand side is $\langle Lf, f \rangle$. We bound the second factor as

$$\sum_{\{u,v\}\in E} |f(u) + f(v)|^2 \leq 2 \sum_{\{u,v\}\in E} \left(f(u)^2 + f(v)^2\right)$$

$$= 2 \sum_v \deg(v) f(v)^2$$

$$\leq 2d \sum_v f(v)^2.$$

The inequalities combine to give $\beta^2 \langle f, f \rangle^2 \leq 2d \langle Lf, f \rangle \langle f, f \rangle$. The claim follows after cancelling $\langle f, f \rangle$.

Step 3. Let g be an eigenfunction for λ_2. By taking the real or the imaginary part, we may assume that g is real valued. Let us refer to a vertex v as positive (or negative) if $g(v) > 0$ (respectively $g(v) < 0$). As g is orthogonal to $\mathbb{1}$, there are both positive and negative vertices. Up to replacing g by $-g$, we may assume that no more than half the vertices are positive. Let f be the positive part of g, that is, the function defined by $f = g$ on positive vertices, and $f = 0$ elsewhere. Then $f(v) \geq g(v)$ for every vertex v, and so $Af(v) \geq Ag(v)$ for every vertex v. At a *positive* vertex v we have

$$Lf(v) = \deg(v)f(v) - Af(v) \leq \deg(v)g(v) - Ag(v) = Lg(v).$$

As f is supported on the positive vertices, where it takes positive values by definition, we have

$$\langle Lf, f \rangle \leq \langle Lg, f \rangle = \lambda_2 \langle g, f \rangle = \lambda_2 \langle f, f \rangle.$$

Combining this bound with the bound from step 2, we conclude that $\beta^2 \leq 2d\lambda_2$. □

The spectral lower bound for the isoperimetric constant (Theorem 11.7) had a very easy proof, and turned out to be very effective in practice. So it is quite ironic that the spectral upper bound of Theorem 11.15, which is significantly harder to prove, is rarely effective in practice. Tested on some families of graphs, it quickly appears to be a fairly bad bound. Both the Paley graphs $P(q)$ and the incidence graphs $I_3(q)$ have $\alpha_2 \sim C\sqrt{d}$ as $q \to \infty$, for some numerical constant C. Thus $\lambda_2 = d - \alpha_2 \sim d$, and $\sqrt{2d\lambda_2} \sim \sqrt{2}d$ as $q \to \infty$. This is worse than the trivial upper bound d. On the cubes Q_n, the performance is also poor: the spectral upper bound is $\sqrt{2d\lambda_2} = 2\sqrt{d}$, whereas the isoperimetric constant is 1. Here, at least, we are beating the combinatorial upper bound of roughly $d/2$.

On the other hand, the spectral upper bound is effective for the cycles C_n: we have $\sqrt{2d\lambda_2} = 4\sin(\pi/n) \sim 4\pi/n$, while iso $C_n \sim 4/n$. Unlike the previous families, the cycles form a family of constant degree.

Recall that an expander family is a d-regular family of graphs whose isoperimetric constant is uniformly bounded away from 0. The conceptual importance of Theorem 11.15 is that, in conjunction with Theorem 11.7, it implies the following: a d-regular family is an expander family if and only if it has a uniform spectral gap. In Laplacian terms, this means that λ_2 is uniformly bounded away from 0; in adjacency terms, α_2 is uniformly bounded away from d. Note, however, that there is a quantitative difference between the combinatorial and the spectral approach to expanders.

Notes. Fiedler (*Algebraic connectivity of graphs*, Czechoslovak Math. J. 1973; Zbl 0265.05119) was the first to seize on the importance of λ_2 in relation to graph connectivity. He called λ_2 the 'algebraic connectivity' of a graph. Fiedler's starting point was the observation that, in the context of possibly disconnected graphs, the connectivity of a graph is equivalent to the condition that $\lambda_2 > 0$.

Theorems 11.15 and 11.7 are graph-theoretic analogues of results due to Cheeger (*A lower bound for the smallest eigenvalue of the Laplacian*, in 'Problems in analysis', Princeton University Press 1970; Zbl 0212.44903), respectively Buser (*A note on the isoperimetric constant*, Ann. Sci. École Norm. Sup. 1982; Zbl 0501.53030), relating the isoperimetric constant of a compact Riemannian manifold M to the first positive eigenvalue of the Laplacian operator on $L^2(M)$. Theorem 11.7 is implicitly due to Alon and Milman (λ_1, *isoperimetric inequalities for graphs, and supercon-centrators*, J. Combin. Theory Ser. B 1985; Zbl 0549.05051). Theorem 11.15, the analogue of Cheeger's result, is due to Dodziuk (*Difference equations, isoperimetric inequality and transience of certain random walks*, Trans. Amer. Math. Soc. 1984; Zbl 0512.39001). See also Mohar (*Isoperimetric numbers of graphs*, J. Combin. Theory Ser. B 1989; Zbl 0719.05042) for an improvement.

Expander families do not come easily. The first explicit construction is due to Margulis (*Explicit constructions of expanders*, Problems Inform. Transmission 1973) and it relies on a rather sophisticated phenomenon, namely Kazhdan's property (T). Margulis's paper is also the starting point for the spectral perspective on expanders.

Another early explicit construction of an expander family is due to Buser (*On the bipartition of graphs*, Discrete Appl. Math. 1984; Zbl 0544.05038). Buser's construction also depends on a spectral perspective, but in a rather different way: as he puts it, his proof is '*very* unorthodox–from the point of view of graph theory–and is in the realm of the spectral geometry of the Laplace operator on Riemann surfaces'.

Remarkably, there are expander families consisting of d-regular graphs with the following property:

all eigenvalues different from $\pm d$ lie in the interval $\left[-2\sqrt{d-1}, 2\sqrt{d-1}\right]$. $\quad(*)$

In light of the Alon–Boppana phenomenon, one cannot pack the eigenvalues of a d-regular family in a smaller interval. On the other hand, the existence of expander families satisfying $(*)$ shows that the Alon–Boppana phenomenon is sharp.

Expander families satisfying $(*)$ were first constructed by Lubotzky, Phillips, Sarnak (*Ramanujan graphs*, Combinatorica 1988; Zbl 0661.05035) and, indepen-dently, Margulis (*Explicit group-theoretical constructions of combinatorial schemes and their application to the design of expanders and concentrators*, Problems Inform. Transmission 1988; Zbl 0708.05030). The graphs in question are Cayley graphs of $\mathrm{PSL}_2(\mathbb{Z}_p)$ or $\mathrm{PGL}_2(\mathbb{Z}_p)$, of degree $\ell + 1$. Here p and ℓ are distinct primes congruent to 1 mod 4, and the choice of PSL_2 or PGL_2 depends on the sign of the Legendre symbol $(p/\ell) = (\ell/p)$. The proof of $(*)$ for these specific graphs rests on a deep number-theoretical fact, the solution of the so-called Ramanujan conjecture. For this reason, expander families satisfying $(*)$ have come to be known as Ramanujan expander families. Simpler and more flexible constructions of Ramanujan expander families are currently known. A very recent and most notable result of Marcus, Spielman, and Srivastava (*Interlacing families I: Bipartite Ramanujan graphs of all degrees*, Ann. of Math. (2) 2015; Zbl 1316.05066) says that Ramanujan expander families can be constructed for all degrees greater than 2.

11.3 Edge counting

Let S and T be two sets of vertices in a regular graph. Denote by $e(S, T)$ the number of edges connecting vertices in S to vertices in T, with the convention that edges having both endpoints in $S \cap T$ are counted twice. We want to estimate the local quantity $e(S, T)$ in terms of the size of S, the size of T, and global information on the graph. It turns out that the spread of the non-trivial eigenvalues of X can be used to control the deviation of $e(S, T)$ from its expected value, (edge density) $\cdot |S| |T|$.

We first do this in the bipartite case.

Theorem 11.16. Let X be a bipartite, d-regular graph of half-size m, and let S and T be vertex subsets lying in different sides of the bipartition. Then

$$\left| e(S, T) - \frac{d}{m} |S| |T| \right| \leq \frac{\alpha_2}{m} \sqrt{|S| |T| (m - |S|) (m - |T|)}. \tag{11.2}$$

In particular, we have

$$\left| e(S, T) - \kappa |S| |T| \right| \leq \alpha_2 \sqrt{|S| |T|} \quad \text{whenever} \quad \frac{d - \alpha_2}{m} \leq \kappa \leq \frac{d + \alpha_2}{m}. \tag{11.3}$$

The constant κ in (11.3) should be thought of as a rounding constant. A generic choice is $\kappa = d/m$, but more convenient choices are usually available in applications.

Proof. Note first that, for the characteristic functions of S and T, we have

$$\langle A \mathbb{1}_S, \mathbb{1}_T \rangle = \sum_{u \sim v} \mathbb{1}_S(u) \mathbb{1}_T(v) = e(S, T).$$

Next, we seek a spectral understanding of the left-hand side. Let

$$d = \alpha_1 > \alpha_2 \geq \cdots \geq \alpha_{n-1} = -\alpha_2 > \alpha_n = -d$$

be the adjacency eigenvalues of X, where $n = 2m$ denotes, as usual, the number of vertices. Also let $\{f_k\}$ be an orthonormal basis of adjacency eigenfunctions. Thus f_1 is a constant equal to $1/\sqrt{n}$, while f_n is $1/\sqrt{n}$ on, say, black vertices, and $-1/\sqrt{n}$ on white vertices. Expand $\mathbb{1}_S$ and $\mathbb{1}_T$ in the eigenbasis as $\mathbb{1}_S = \sum s_k f_k$, respectively $\mathbb{1}_T = \sum t_k f_k$. Then

$$\langle A \mathbb{1}_S, \mathbb{1}_T \rangle = \sum_{k=1}^{n} \alpha_k s_k \bar{t}_k.$$

We separate the terms corresponding to the extremal eigenvalues $\pm d$, and the terms corresponding to the intermediate eigenvalues. If, say, S consists of black vertices and T consists of white vertices, then the extremal coefficients are

$$s_1 = \frac{1}{\sqrt{n}} |S| = s_n, \qquad t_1 = \frac{1}{\sqrt{n}} |T| = -t_n.$$

and so

$$\alpha_1 s_1 \bar{t}_1 + \alpha_n s_n \bar{t}_n = \frac{d}{m} |S| |T|.$$

For the intermediate coefficients, we note that

$$\sum_{k=2}^{n-1} |s_k|^2 = \langle \mathbb{1}_S, \mathbb{1}_S \rangle - |s_1|^2 - |s_n|^2 = |S| - \frac{|S|^2}{m} = \frac{1}{m} |S|(m - |S|),$$

and similarly for the coefficients of T. Therefore, by Cauchy–Schwarz we have

$$\sum_{k=2}^{n-1} |s_k| |t_k| \le \frac{1}{m} \sqrt{|S| |T|(m - |S|)(m - |T|)}.$$

Now

$$\left| e(S, T) - \frac{d}{m} |S| |T| \right| = \left| \sum_{k=2}^{n-1} \alpha_k s_k t_k \right| \le \sum_{k=2}^{n-1} |\alpha_k| |s_k| |t_k| \le \alpha_2 \sum_{k=2}^{n-1} |s_k| |t_k|$$

and (11.2) follows. Finally, using $\sqrt{(m - |S|)(m - |T|)} \le m - \sqrt{|S| |T|}$ we get

$$\frac{d + \alpha_2}{m} |S| |T| - \alpha_2 \sqrt{|S| |T|} \le e(S, T) \le \frac{d - \alpha_2}{m} |S| |T| + \alpha_2 \sqrt{|S| |T|},$$

which implies (11.3).   □

The non-bipartite case can be easily derived.

Corollary 11.17. Let X be a non-bipartite, d-regular graph of size n, and let S and T be vertex subsets. Then

$$\left| e(S, T) - \frac{d}{n} |S| |T| \right| \le \frac{\alpha}{n} \sqrt{|S| |T| |S^c| |T^c|}, \quad \alpha := \max\{\alpha_2, -\alpha_n\}.$$

Proof. Let X' be the bipartite double of X. Then $\alpha = \max\{\alpha_2, -\alpha_n\}$ is the second largest eigenvalue of X'. Viewing S and T as vertex subsets of X' of different colours, we may apply (11.2) to get the claimed bound.   □

Theorem 11.16 provides a versatile method, with numerous combinatorial applications.

Example 11.18. Let $\mathbb{F}$ be a finite field with q elements, and let $A, B, C, D \subseteq \mathbb{F}$. The question we wish to address is that of estimating the number of solutions $(a, b, c, d) \in A \times B \times C \times D$ to the following two equations: $a + b = cd$, respectively $ab + cd = 1$.

The hypersurface $\{x+y = zt\} \subseteq \mathbb{F}^4$ has $q^3 = \frac{1}{q}|\mathbb{F}^4|$ points, while the hypersurface $\{xy + zt = 1\} \subseteq \mathbb{F}^4$ has $(q^2 - 1)(q - 1) \sim \frac{1}{q}|\mathbb{F}^4|$ points. So, for both equations we would expect about $\frac{1}{q}|W|$ solutions in the 'window' $W := A \times B \times C \times D \subseteq \mathbb{F}^4$. We will now show that the error in making this estimate is on the order of $\sqrt{|W|}$. More precisely, we show that the number of restricted solutions N_W to either one of the two equations satisfies the bound

$$\left|N_W - \frac{1}{q}|W|\right| \leq \sqrt{q|W|}.$$

We work in the orthogonal picture of the incidence graph $I_3(q)$, which has $m = q^2 + q + 1$, $d = q + 1$, $\alpha_2 = \sqrt{q}$. So we may use $\kappa = 1/q$ in (11.3).

For the equation $a+b = cd$, let S be the set of black vertices of the form $[(a, -1, c)]_\bullet$ with $a \in A$ and $c \in C$, and let T be the set of white vertices of the form $[(-1, b, d)]_\circ$ with $b \in B$ and $d \in D$. Thus $|S||T| = |A||C||B||D| = |W|$. Furthermore, there is an edge between $[(a, -1, c)]_\bullet$ and $[(-1, b, d)]_\circ$ precisely when $a + b = cd$, so $e(S, T)$ counts the number of solutions in $W = A \times B \times C \times D$ to the equation $a + b = cd$. An application of (11.3) yields the desired estimate.

For the equation $ab + cd = 1$, take S to be the set of black vertices of the form $[(1, a, c)]_\bullet$ with $a \in A$ and $c \in C$, and T to be the set of white vertices of the form $[(-1, b, d)]_\circ$ with $b \in B$ and $d \in D$.

Example 11.19. Let $\mathbb{F}$ be a field with q elements, where q is odd. Let $A, B \subseteq \mathbb{F}$ have the property that the sum-set $A + B = \{a + b : a \in A, b \in B\}$ consists of squares. Then $|A||B| \leq q$.

Before giving the argument, let us note that the bound is sharp: take $\mathbb{F}$ to be a field with q^2 elements, and A and B to be the subfield of $\mathbb{F}$ having q elements.

As our ambient graph X, we take the bi-Cayley graph of the additive group of $\mathbb{F}$ with respect to $\mathbb{F}^2$, the subset of squares. Recall that X is a bipartite graph whose vertex set consists of two copies of $\mathbb{F}$, in which an edge connects $x_\bullet$ to $y_\circ$ whenever $x + y$ is a square. By viewing A and B as vertex subsets of different colours, the hypothesis means that X contains a copy of the complete bipartite graph $K_{|A|,|B|}$.

The next step is a rather general application of (11.3): if a regular bipartite graph contains the complete bipartite graph $K_{s,t}$, then

$$\sqrt{st} \leq \frac{m}{1 + (m - d)/\alpha_2}. \tag{11.4}$$

Our graph X has $m = q$, $d = \frac{1}{2}(q + 1)$ and, as we show below, $\alpha_2 \leq \frac{1}{2}(\sqrt{q} + 1)$. Using these values in (11.4), we obtain $st \leq q$ after a short and pleasant computation.

The graph X is a close relative of the bi-Paley graph. In order to estimate the adjacency eigenvalues, we recall and adapt Example 8.9. Let ψ be a non-trivial additive character. Then

$$\alpha_\psi = \sum_{s \in \mathbb{F}^2} \psi(s) = 1 + \sum_{s \in (\mathbb{F}^*)^2} \psi(s) = \frac{1}{2}(G(\psi, \sigma) + 1),$$

where σ is the quadratic character. Hence

$$|\alpha_\psi| \le \frac{1}{2}(|G(\psi, \sigma)| + 1) = \frac{1}{2}(\sqrt{q} + 1),$$

as claimed.

Example 11.20. Let $\mathbb{F}$ be a field with q elements, and assume that a proportion $\epsilon \in (0, 1)$ of lines, respectively planes in $\mathbb{F}^3$, is selected. We wish to address the following question: how large should ϵ be, so as to guarantee that some selected line is contained in some selected plane?

The graph underlying the combinatorics is, of course, the incidence graph $I_3(q)$. We need a lower bound on ϵ so that there is an edge between S and T, whenever S and T are two collections of lines and planes with $|S| = |T| = \epsilon m$. Applying (11.2), we get

$$\left| e(S, T) - \epsilon^2 dm \right| \le \alpha_2 \epsilon (1 - \epsilon)m.$$

So we may guarantee that $e(S, T) > 0$ by imposing the condition $\epsilon^2 d > \alpha_2 \epsilon(1 - \epsilon)$. This amounts to

$$\epsilon > \frac{1}{1 + d/\alpha_2}.$$

Now $I_3(q)$ has $d = q + 1$ and $\alpha_2 = \sqrt{q}$. So it suffices to have

$$\epsilon \ge \frac{1}{1 + \sqrt{q}}.$$

Exercise 11.21. Let X be a d-regular graph of size n, and let S be a vertex subset of size ϵn. Show that the average degree of the subgraph induced by S can be bounded as

$$\epsilon d + (1 - \epsilon)\alpha_n \le d_{\text{ave}}(S) \le \epsilon d + (1 - \epsilon)\alpha_2.$$

Theorem 11.16 can be extended in several directions. For example, we can weaken the regularity assumption.

Theorem 11.22. Let X be a biregular bipartite graph, with bipartition $X_\bullet \cup X_\circ$. Let $d_\bullet$ and $d_\circ$ denote the degrees of each black, respectively white vertex, and let $m_\bullet$ and $m_\circ$ denote the numbers of black, respectively white vertices.

If S is a vertex subset of $X_\bullet$, and T is a vertex subset of $X_\circ$, then the following holds:

$$\left| e(S, T) - \sqrt{\frac{d_\bullet d_\circ}{m_\bullet m_\circ}} |S| |T| \right| \le \alpha_2 \sqrt{|S| |T| \left(1 - \frac{|S|}{m_\bullet}\right)\left(1 - \frac{|T|}{m_\circ}\right)}.$$

Corollary 11.23. Let X be a biregular bipartite graph, with $X_\bullet$, $m_\bullet$, $d_\bullet$ and $X_\circ$, $m_\circ$, $d_\circ$ as above.

Let S be a vertex subset of $X_\bullet$, and let $N(S)$ be the set of those vertices in $X_\circ$ which are adjacent to some vertex in S. If $|S| = \epsilon m_\bullet$, then $|N(S)| \geq \delta m_\circ$ for

$$\delta = \frac{\epsilon}{\epsilon + (1 - \epsilon)\frac{\alpha_2^2}{d_\bullet d_\circ}}.$$

In another direction, we could count paths instead of edges. For two vertex subsets S and T in a graph, we denote by $p_\ell(S, T)$ the number of paths of length ℓ connecting vertices in S to vertices in T.

Theorem 11.24. Let X be a bipartite d-regular graph of half-size m, and let S and T be vertex subsets. Assume that either ℓ is odd, and S and T have different colours, or ℓ is even, and S and T have the same colour. Then

$$\left| p_\ell(S, T) - \frac{d^\ell}{m}|S|\,|T| \right| \leq \frac{\alpha_2^\ell}{m}\sqrt{|S|\,|T|(m - |S|)(m - |T|)}.$$

Corollary 11.25. Let X be a non-bipartite d-regular graph of size n, and let S and T be vertex subsets. Then

$$\left| p_\ell(S, T) - \frac{d^\ell}{n}|S|\,|T| \right| \leq \frac{\alpha^\ell}{n}\sqrt{|S|\,|T|\,|S^c|\,|T^c|}, \quad \alpha := \max\{\alpha_2, -\alpha_n\}.$$

Exercise 11.26. If X is a non-bipartite d-regular graph of size n, then

$$\mathrm{diam}\, X \leq \frac{\log(n - 1)}{\log(d/\alpha)} + 1, \quad \alpha := \max\{\alpha_2, -\alpha_n\}.$$

If X is a bipartite d-regular graph of half-size m, then

$$\mathrm{diam}\, X \leq \frac{\log(m - 1)}{\log(d/\alpha_2)} + 2.$$

Notes. Theorem 11.16 and Corollary 11.17 are slight variations on a result due to Alon and Chung (*Explicit construction of linear sized tolerant networks*, Discrete Math. 1988; Zbl 0657.05068). A conceptual precursor is Thomason's notion of jumbled graphs (*Pseudorandom graphs*, in 'Random graphs '85', North-Holland 1987; Zbl 0626.00008).

The estimates in Example 11.18 are inspired by, and partially improve, estimates due to Gyarmati and Sárközy (*Equations in finite fields with restricted solution sets II (Algebraic equations)*, Acta Math. Hungar. 2008; Zbl 1199.11141).

Corollary 11.23 is due to Tanner (*Explicit concentrators from generalized N-gons*, SIAM J. Algebraic Discrete Methods 1984; Zbl 0554.05045).

Exercise 11.26 is a result due to Chung (*Diameters and eigenvalues*, J. Amer. Math. Soc. 1989; Zbl 0678.05037).

12

Farewell

This final chapter serves as a brief review. We motivate, introduce, and then study a new graph — firstly, as a way to revisit some of the ideas, facts, and methods we have seen, and secondly, in order to add an interesting irregular example to our stock, which mostly consisted of regular graphs.

12.1 Graphs without 4-cycles

A rich theme in extremal graph theory is that of bounding the number of edges in graphs with a forbidden subgraph. This theme is, in fact, two-sided: on the one hand, one proves upper bounds, usually by combinatorial arguments; on the other hand, one gives constructions showing how these bounds are attained, or nearly attained.

The earliest example of this theme is that of graphs without 3-cycles; see Exercises 1.2 and 1.5. Turán's theorem 9.11 is concerned with graphs without a fixed complete subgraph. For graphs without 4-cycles, the following holds.

Theorem 12.1 (Reiman). If a graph on n vertices does not contain C_4 as a subgraph, then the number of edges can be bounded as

$$|E| \le \frac{n}{4}\left(\sqrt{4n-3}+1\right).$$

Recall that Turán's theorem had a stronger, spectral version — Theorem 9.12 — involving the largest adjacency eigenvalue. The previous theorem has a spectral strengthening as well.

Theorem 12.2 (Nikiforov). If a graph on n vertices does not contain C_4 as a subgraph, then its largest adjacency eigenvalue satisfies

$$\alpha_{\max} \le \frac{1}{2}\left(\sqrt{4n-3}+1\right).$$

Proof. Let f be a positive eigenfunction for $\alpha_{\max}$. Then for each vertex v we have

$$A^2 f(v) = \sum_{u:u\sim v} Af(u) \le \deg(v)f(v) + \sum_{w\ne v} f(w)$$

since, for each vertex $w \neq v$, there is at most one 2-path joining it to v. Summing the previous inequality over all vertices, we get

$$\sum_v A^2 f(v) \leq \sum_v \deg(v) f(v) + (n-1) \sum_v f(v).$$

Using

$$\sum_v A^2 f(v) = \alpha_{\max}^2 \sum_v f(v),$$

$$\sum_v \deg(v) f(v) = \langle A\mathbb{1}, f \rangle = \langle \mathbb{1}, Af \rangle = \alpha_{\max} \langle \mathbb{1}, f \rangle = \alpha_{\max} \sum_v f(v),$$

we deduce that $\alpha_{\max}^2 \leq \alpha_{\max} + (n-1)$. The desired bound for $\alpha_{\max}$ immediately follows.   □

For a graph to attain the above spectral bound, each vertex v must have exactly one common neighbour with any other vertex $w \neq v$. According to the friendship theorem 8.16, such a graph is a windmill graph. And conversely, a windmill graph attains the above spectral bound, by Exercise 7.13.

But windmill graphs do not attain the edge bound of Theorem 12.1. The one exception is the unique regular windmill graph, the 3-cycle. The failure of the edge bound is even more conspicuous from an asymptotic perspective: the number of edges of a windmill graph on n vertices is linear in n, more specifically $|E| \sim \frac{3}{2} n$.

12.2 The Erdős–Rényi graph

Let $\mathbb{F}$ be a finite field with q elements. Consider the graph whose vertices are the lines through the origin in the 3-dimensional space $\mathbb{F}^3$, and edges encode orthogonality with respect to the standard scalar product. In other words, the vertex set is the projective space $\mathbb{F}^3 \setminus \{0\}$ mod $\mathbb{F}^*$, and edges connect two distinct vertices $[x_1, x_2, x_3]$ and $[y_1, y_2, y_3]$ whenever $x_1 y_1 + x_2 y_2 + x_3 y_3 = 0$. This is the so-called *Erdős–Rényi graph*, denoted $ER(q)$.

Proposition 12.3. The graph $ER(q)$ has $q^2 + q + 1$ vertices, of which q^2 have degree $q + 1$, and $q + 1$ have degree q. The graph $ER(q)$ has diameter 2 and contains no 4-cycles; in other words, any two distinct vertices have at most one common neighbour.

Note that, with the vertex degrees at hand, we can derive the number of edges of $ER(q)$. As a function of the number of vertices $n = q^2 + q + 1$, we can write

$$|E| = \frac{n-1}{4} \left(\sqrt{4n - 3} + 1 \right).$$

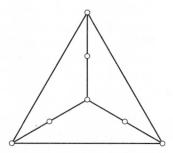

Figure 12.1. The Erdős–Rényi graph for $q = 2$.

This shows that the bound of Theorem 12.1 is asymptotically sharp.

Proof. The number of vertices is clear: there are $(q^3 - 1)/(q - 1) = q^2 + q + 1$ lines through the origin in $\mathbb{F}^3$. Given a line ℓ, its orthogonal space $\ell^\perp$ is a plane through the origin in $\mathbb{F}^3$. So there are $(q^2 - 1)/(q - 1) = q + 1$ lines orthogonal to ℓ, but one of them could be ℓ itself. This means that a vertex in $ER(q)$ has degree $q + 1$ or q. A vertex $[x_1, x_2, x_3]$ has degree q precisely when

$$x_1^2 + x_2^2 + x_3^2 = 0. \tag{12.1}$$

In order to show that there are $q + 1$ such 'singular' vertices $[x_1, x_2, x_3]$, we need to argue that equation (12.1) has q^2 solutions (x_1, x_2, x_3) in $\mathbb{F}^3$.

If q is even, then $x_1^2 + x_2^2 + x_3^2 = (x_1 + x_2 + x_3)^2$, so (12.1) amounts to $x_1 + x_2 + x_3 = 0$. The latter equation has q^2 solutions in $\mathbb{F}^3$. Assume now that q is odd. The solutions with $x_1 \neq 0$ are of the form (x_1, ax_1, bx_1), where $a^2 + b^2 = -1$. Recalling Proposition 5.5, we obtain $(q-1)(q-\sigma(-1))$ solutions in this case. The solutions with $x_1 = 0$ are of the form $(0, a, b)$, where $a^2 + b^2 = 0$. Considering the two possibilities, that -1 is a square or not, we find $q + \sigma(-1)(q - 1)$ solutions in this case. Adding, there are q^2 solutions, as claimed.

Let us consider the second statement. A common neighbour of two distinct vertices ℓ and ℓ' represents a line orthogonal to the plane spanned by ℓ and ℓ'. Since the orthogonal space of a plane is just a line, there is at most one such common neighbour. So $ER(q)$ contains no 4-cycles. If ℓ and ℓ' are not orthogonal, then the line orthogonal to both ℓ and ℓ' is different from ℓ and ℓ'. In graph-theoretic terms, two non-adjacent vertices in $ER(q)$ have a common neighbour, so $ER(q)$ has diameter 2. $\qquad\square$

It may happen that two distinct vertices in $ER(q)$ have no common neighbour. Indeed, if ℓ is a singular vertex and ℓ' is an adjacent vertex, then they have no common neighbour since the line orthogonal to both ℓ and ℓ' is ℓ itself. Alternatively, we might argue by contradiction. If we assume that any two distinct vertices in $ER(q)$ have at least one common neighbour, then such a common neighbour has to be unique. The friendship theorem 8.16 will then imply that $ER(q)$ is a windmill graph, which is certainly not true: there is no vertex of degree $q^2 + q + 1$ in $ER(q)$.

A closer look at the pattern of common neighbours reveals the following:

Proposition 12.4. The graph $ER(q)$ has the property that any two distinct non-adjacent vertices have $c = 1$ common neighbours, and any two adjacent vertices have $\bar{c} = q^2 - q$ common non-neighbours.

Proof. The first part, concerning non-adjacent vertices, already appears in the proof of the previous proposition. Let us focus on the second part.

In a graph on n vertices, the number of common non-neighbours of two vertices u and v is given by $n - (\deg(u) + \deg(v) - c_{uv})$, where c_{uv} counts the number of common neighbours. So we have to check that, in $ER(q)$, any two adjacent vertices ℓ and ℓ' satisfy $\deg(\ell) + \deg(\ell') - c_{\ell\ell'} = 2q + 1$. If both ℓ and ℓ' are non-singular, then $\deg(\ell) = \deg(\ell') = q + 1$, and $c_{\ell\ell'} = 1$. If one of them, say ℓ, is singular, then ℓ' must be non-singular. In this case $\deg(\ell) = q$, $\deg(\ell') = q + 1$, and $c_{\ell\ell'} = 0$. □

A graph enjoying the combinatorial property of the previous proposition will be referred to as a *DH-graph* with parameters c and $\bar{c}$. The class of DH-graphs generalizes the class of strongly regular graphs — more precisely, the regular DH-graphs are the strongly regular graphs. This is a good point to make the following notational remark: the parameter c for DH-graphs has the same meaning as for strongly regular graphs, while the parameter $\bar{c}$ should be interpreted as c for the complement graph. The main novelty lies in irregular DH-graphs. The Erdős–Rényi graph $ER(q)$ provides an interesting example, but there are others. A star graph is a DH-graph, with parameters $c = 1$ and $\bar{c} = 0$. The cone over a DH-graph with parameters $c = k$, $\bar{c} = 0$ is a DH-graph with parameters $c = k + 1$, $\bar{c} = 0$.

12.3 Eigenvalues of the Erdős–Rényi graph

In Theorem 8.11, we saw how to compute the eigenvalues of strongly regular graphs. The following is a generalization to DH-graphs.

Theorem 12.5. A DH-graph has three distinct Laplacian eigenvalues. The two non-trivial Laplacian eigenvalues are given, in terms of the parameters c and $\bar{c}$, and the size n, by

$$\lambda + \lambda' = c + n - \bar{c}, \qquad \lambda\lambda' = cn. \qquad (12.2)$$

Proof. We will check that the Laplacian matrix L satisfies

$$L^2 - (c + n - \bar{c})L + cnI = cJ. \tag{12.3}$$

Assume that we have (12.3). Let λ be a non-trivial Laplacian eigenvalue, and let g be a corresponding eigenfunction. Then g is orthogonal to $\mathbb{1}$, an eigenfunction of the trivial eigenvalue 0, and so $Jg = 0$. Applying (12.3) to g, we find that $\lambda^2 - (c + n - \bar{c})\lambda + cn = 0$. This quadratic equation is equivalent to the relations (12.2).

We verify (12.3) entrywise. Off-diagonally, it amounts to

$$L^2(u, v) - (c + n - \bar{c})L(u, v) = c \tag{*}$$

whenever u and v are distinct. Now

$$L^2(u, v) = \sum_w L(u, w)L(w, v) = \deg(u)L(u, v) + \deg(v)L(u, v) + c_{uv},$$

where, we recall, c_{uv} denotes the number of common neighbours. If u and v are non-adjacent, then $L(u, v) = 0$ and $L^2(u, v) = c_{uv} = c$ so (*) holds. If u and v are adjacent, then $L(u, v) = -1$ and $L^2(u, v) = -\deg(u) - \deg(v) + c_{uv} = \bar{c} - n$, so (*) holds in this case as well.

Diagonally, (12.3) claims that

$$L^2(u, u) - (c + n - \bar{c})L(u, u) + cn = c \tag{**}$$

for any vertex u. Now $L(u, u) = \deg(u)$ and $L^2(u, u) = \deg(u)^2 + \deg(u)$, and we rewrite (**) as

$$\deg(u)\big(n - 1 - \deg(u) - \bar{c}\big) = c\big(n - 1 - \deg(u)\big) \tag{**$'$}$$

Let C be the set of neighbours of u, and D the set of non-neighbours of u. The combinatorial meaning of (**$'$) is that it counts the edges between C and D. Indeed, we have $|C| = \deg(u)$ and $|D| = n - 1 - \deg(u)$. Each vertex in D has c neighbours in C, so the right-hand side of (**$'$) counts the edges from D towards C. Each vertex w in C has $\bar{c}$ common non-neighbours with u, all of which lie in D. The remaining $n - 1 - \deg(u) - \bar{c}$ vertices from D are neighbours of w. Thus, the left-hand side of (**$'$) counts the edges from C towards D. □

Let us point out that, in the course of the previous proof, we also showed that vertex degrees in a DH-graph can take only two values. Indeed, by (**$'$), vertex degrees are solutions of a quadratic equation.

Once we know the eigenvalues λ and λ', we can find their multiplicities by solving

$$1 + m + m' = n, \qquad \lambda m + \lambda'm' = \sum \deg(v). \tag{12.4}$$

Let us focus again on the Erdős–Rényi graph $ER(q)$. Feeding the data from Propositions 12.3 and 12.4 into the relations (12.2) and (12.4), we derive the following:

Proposition 12.6. The non-trivial Laplacian eigenvalues of $ER(q)$ are $q + 1 \pm \sqrt{q}$, each with multiplicity $\frac{1}{2}(q^2 + q)$.

On the adjacency side, the spectral picture is slightly blurry.

Proposition 12.7. The largest adjacency eigenvalue of $ER(q)$ satisfies the bound

$$q + 1 - \frac{1}{q} < \alpha_{\max} < q + 1.$$

The remaining adjacency eigenvalues lie in $\left[- \sqrt{q} - 1, -\sqrt{q} \right] \cup \left[\sqrt{q} - 1, \sqrt{q} \right]$.

Proof. We have $d_{\text{ave}} < \alpha_{\max} < q + 1$ by Theorem 9.6. The average degree can be computed explicitly, and then some simplifying estimates lead to the lower bound $d_{\text{ave}} > q + 1 - 1/q$.

For the remaining $q^2 + q$ adjacency eigenvalues, we appeal to Proposition 10.9. This is especially convenient for $ER(q)$ since the minimal and the maximal degrees differ by 1 only. The bound $q \leq \alpha_k + \lambda_k \leq q + 1$, combined with Proposition 12.6 above, implies that $\frac{1}{2}(q^2 + q)$ adjacency eigenvalues lie in $\left[- \sqrt{q} - 1, -\sqrt{q} \right]$, and $\frac{1}{2}(q^2 + q)$ adjacency eigenvalues lie in $\left[\sqrt{q} - 1, \sqrt{q} \right]$.   □

Here is another possible approach to bounding the remaining adjacency eigenvalues of $ER(q)$. The bipartite double of $ER(q)$ is a spanning subgraph of the incidence graph $I_3(q)$, obtained by removing $q+1$ disjoint edges. This is the situation addressed by Theorem 10.15. It quickly becomes apparent, however, that this approach leads to weaker bounds than the ones provided above.

To put the previous proposition into perspective, let us mention that the adjacency eigenvalues of $ER(q)$ are, in fact, known. They are the roots of the polynomial

$$(X^3 - qX^2 - 2qX + q^2 + q)(X^2 + X + 1 - q)^q (X^2 - q)^{\frac{1}{2}(q^2 - q) - 1}.$$

The last quadratic factor gives the eigenvalues $\pm\sqrt{q}$, each with multiplicity $\frac{1}{2}(q^2 - q) - 1$. The middle quadratic factor gives an eigenvalue α^- in $\left(- \sqrt{q} - 1, -\sqrt{q} \right)$ with multiplicity q, and an eigenvalue α^+ in $\left(\sqrt{q} - 1, \sqrt{q} \right)$ with multiplicity q. The eigenvalues $\alpha^\pm$ are explicit, approximately equal to $\pm\sqrt{q} - \frac{1}{2}$. The roots of the cubic factor are less obvious. By checking the sign change, it can be seen that it has a root in $\left(\alpha^+, \sqrt{q} \right)$, and a root in $\left(- \sqrt{q} - 1, \alpha^- \right)$. This latter root is $\alpha_{\min}$. The cubic factor has one more root, and this is $\alpha_{\max}$. Checking the change of sign reveals that

$$q + 1 - \frac{1}{q} < \alpha_{\max} < q + 1 - \frac{1}{q + 1}.$$

We end by discussing spectral bounds on the chromatic and the independence numbers of the Erdős–Rényi graph. By Proposition 2.2, we have the degree bound

$$\text{chr } ER(q) \leq q + 1 \tag{12.5}$$

and we note that Wilf's spectral upper bound (Theorem 11.1) leads to the same conclusion.

Combining Hoffman's spectral lower bound (Theorem 11.2) with the estimates $\alpha_{\min} \geq -(\sqrt{q} + 1)$, $\alpha_{\max} > q - 1$ afforded by Proposition 12.7, we get

$$\text{chr } ER(q) > \sqrt{q}. \tag{12.6}$$

Finally, we apply Hoffman's upper bound for the independence number (Theorem 11.4). Plugging in $n = q^2 + q + 1$, $d_{\min} = q$, and $\lambda_{\max} = q + 1 + \sqrt{q}$, yields the following result.

Proposition 12.8. The independence number of $ER(q)$ satisfies

$$\text{ind } ER(q) \leq q\sqrt{q} + 1.$$

The chromatic bound (12.6) can actually be deduced from the above independence bound, via the general inequality $\text{chr} \cdot \text{ind} \geq n$. The same inequality, combined with (12.5), leads to $\text{ind } ER(q) \geq q + 1$. This, however, is not hard to see directly: the $q + 1$ singular vertices of $ER(q)$ form an independent set.

Notes. The reference for Theorem 12.1 is Reiman (*Über ein Problem von K. Zaran-kiewicz*, Acta. Math. Acad. Sci. Hungar. 1958; Zbl 0084.01303). Theorem 12.2 is an instance of a more general result of Nikiforov (*Bounds on graph eigenvalues. II*, Linear Algebra Appl. 2007; Zbl 1128.05035).

The graph $ER(q)$ was introduced by Erdős and Rényi (*On a problem in the theory of graphs*, Magyar Tud. Akad. Mat. Kutató Int. Közl. 1962) and, later on, independently by Brown (*On graphs that do not contain a Thomsen graph*, Canad. Math. Bull. 1966; Zbl 0178.27302). Brown and, at roughly the same time, Erdős, Rényi, and Sós (*On a problem of graph theory*, Studia Sci. Math. Hungar. 1966; Zbl 0144.23302) observed that $ER(q)$ witnesses the asymptotic sharpness of Reiman's bound. Historically, this is the first instance of a striking phenomenon — namely, that a great number of examples in extremal graph theory use geometric and algebraic aspects of finite fields.

DH-graphs were studied by van Dam and Haemers (*Graphs with constant μ and $\bar{\mu}$*, Discrete Math. 1998; Zbl 0901.05068), hence the name adopted herein. Among other things, they prove Theorem 12.5.

The computation of the adjacency spectrum of $ER(q)$ is due to Godsil and Royle (unpublished), and it is quoted by Godsil and Newman (*Eigenvalue bounds for independent sets*, J. Combin. Theory Ser. B 2008; Zbl 1156.05041).

It turns out that the bound of Proposition 12.8, on the independence number, has the correct order of magnitude. Mubayi and Williford (*On the independence number of the Erdős–Rényi and projective norm graphs and a related hypergraph*, J. Graph Theory 2007; Zbl 1128.05040) showed that $\operatorname{ind} ER(q) \geq Cq\sqrt{q}$ for some explicit constant $C > 0$.

Further reading

Noga Alon
Tools from higher algebra, in 'Handbook of combinatorics', 1749–1783, Elsevier 1995. Zbl 0848.05073

László Babai and Peter Frankl
Linear algebra methods in combinatorics, Preliminary version, University of Chicago 1992.

Simeon Ball
Finite geometry and combinatorial applications, London Mathematical Society Student Texts no. 82, Cambridge University Press 2015. Zbl 1352.05001

Béla Bollobás
Modern graph theory, Graduate Texts in Mathematics no. 184, Springer 1998. Zbl 0902.05016

Andries E. Brouwer and Willem H. Haemers
Spectra of graphs, Universitext, Springer 2012. Zbl 1231.05001

Peter J. Cameron and Jack H. van Lint
Designs, graphs, codes and their links, London Mathematical Society Student Texts no. 22, Cambridge University Press 1991. Zbl 0743.05004

Fan Chung
Spectral graph theory, CBMS Series in Mathematics no. 92, American Mathematical Society 1997. Zbl 0867.05046

Giuliana Davidoff, Peter Sarnak, and Alain Valette
Elementary number theory, group theory, and Ramanujan graphs, London Mathematical Society Student Texts no. 55, Cambridge University Press 2003. Zbl 1032.11001

Chris Godsil and Gordon Royle
Algebraic graph theory, Graduate Texts in Mathematics no. 207, Springer 2001. Zbl 0968.05002

Shlomo Hoory, Nathan Linial, and Avi Wigderson
Expander graphs and their applications, Bull. Amer. Math. Soc. 43 (2006), 439–561. Zbl 1147.68608

Stasys Jukna
Extremal combinatorics. With applications in computer science, Second edition,
Texts in Theoretical Computer Science. An EATCS Series, Springer 2011.
Zbl 1239.05001

Jiří Matoušek
Thirty-three miniatures. Mathematical and algorithmic applications of linear algebra, Student Mathematical Library no. 53, American Mathematical Society 2010.
Zbl 1195.00043

Daniel Spielman
Spectral graph theory, in 'Combinatorial scientific computing', 495–524, CRC Press
2012. Zbl 1235.68008

Solutions to exercises

Chapter 1

1.2. Let u and v be adjacent vertices. Then $\deg(u) + \deg(v) \leq n$, as u and v have no common neighbours. Summing over all the adjacent pairs, we get

$$2n|E| \geq \sum_{u \sim v} \deg(u) + \deg(v) = 2 \sum_{v \in V} \deg(v)^2.$$

On the other hand,

$$n \sum_{v \in V} \deg(v)^2 \geq \left(\sum_{v \in V} \deg(v) \right)^2 = 4|E|^2,$$

and the desired bound, $|E| \leq n^2/4$, follows.

1.3. Label the vertices as in Figure S.1.

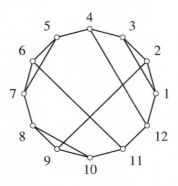

Figure S.1.

There are two types of links: ○ ○ ○ for the vertices labelled 4, 11, 12, and ○–○ ○ for the other vertices. An automorphism must permute 4, 11, 12; in fact it fixes 12, whereas 4 and 11 are either fixed or flipped. Note that 1 is fixed as well. Since 1 and 4 have a common neighbour different from 12, while 1 and 11 do not, it follows that 4 and 11 must be fixed. Consequently, 3 and then 2 are also fixed. Similarly, one sees that the remaining vertices are fixed as well.

1.5. If n is even, say $n = 2m$, then $K_{m,m}$ has n vertices and $m^2 = \lfloor n^2/4 \rfloor$ edges. If n is odd, say $n = 2m + 1$, then $K_{m,m+1}$ has n vertices and $m(m + 1) = \lfloor n^2/4 \rfloor$ edges. Let us argue that these are the only possible graphs.

Consider a triangle-free graph with n vertices and $\lfloor n^2/4 \rfloor$ edges. If $\deg(u) + \deg(v) \le n - 1$ for all adjacent vertices u and v, then the argument of Exercise 1.2 shows that $|E| \le n(n - 1)/4 < \lfloor n^2/4 \rfloor$. So, there is some adjacent pair satisfying $\deg(u) + \deg(v) = n$. This means that every vertex is adjacent to either u or v, but not both since there are no triangles. We get a partition of the graph into the set of neighbours of u and the set of neighbours of v. This is, in fact, a bipartition thanks to the no-triangles assumption. The two parts have size $\deg(u)$, respectively $\deg(v)$, so

$$|E| \le \deg(u) \cdot \deg(v) \le (\deg(u) + \deg(v))^2/4 = n^2/4.$$

In order to have $|E| = \lfloor n^2/4 \rfloor$, it must be that $\deg(u)$ and $\deg(v)$ are as equal as possible. This gives the complete bipartite graphs pointed out before.

Chapter 2

2.10. In K_n, we have $|\partial S| = |S|(n - |S|)$ for every S. Therefore iso $K_n = \lceil n/2 \rceil$, and any choice of no more than half the vertices is an isoperimetric set.

In C_n, each connected component of S contributes 2 edges to ∂S, so any path of length $\lfloor n/2 \rfloor$ is an isoperimetric set. Therefore iso $C_n = 2/\lfloor n/2 \rfloor$.

In $K_{n,n}$, the boundary of a vertex subset S with b 'black' vertices and w 'white' vertices has size $|\partial S| = b(n - w) + w(n - b) = n|S| - 2bw$. Therefore

$$\text{iso } K_{n,n} = n - \max_{b+w \le n} \frac{2bw}{b + w}.$$

A quick analysis shows that $\beta(K_{n,n}) = n/2$ if n is even, respectively $n/2 + 1/2n$ if n is odd.

For the Petersen graph, note first that a subset S of vertices which induces a 5-cycle has one boundary edge per vertex, that is, $|\partial S|/|S| = 1$. Therefore iso ≤ 1. To show that iso ≥ 1, we need to argue that $|\partial S| \ge |S|$. Since the Petersen graph has girth 5, any subset S of size at most 5 is either a disjoint union of trees, or a 5-cycle. In the latter case, every vertex of S has two edges inside S and one boundary edge, so $|\partial S| = |S|$. If S is a disjoint union of trees, then it has at most $|S| - 1$ internal edges, hence $|\partial S| \ge 3|S| - (|S| - 1) = 2|S| + 1 > |S|$.

2.12. Edges in the boundary of a ball $B_{r-1}(u)$ have the external endpoint in the sphere $S_r(u)$, so $|\partial B_{r-1}(u)| \le d|S_r(u)|$. Assuming $|B_{r-1}(u)| \le n/2$, we get

$$\beta|B_{r-1}(u)| \le |\partial B_{r-1}(u)| \le d|S_r(u)|.$$

Dividing through by d and adding $|B_{r-1}(u)|$ to both sides yields $c|B_{r-1}(u)| \leq |B_r(u)|$, where $c = 1 + \beta/d$. It follows that $c^r \leq |B_r(u)|$.

Now let u and v be vertices with $\text{dist}(u, v) = \text{diam } X$. Let $r \geq 1$ be the largest radius such that $|B_{r-1}(u)| \leq n/2$, and let $s \geq 1$ be the largest radius such that $|B_{s-1}(v)| \leq n/2$. By the previous step, we have $r - 1 \leq \log_c |B_{r-1}(u)| \leq \log_c(n/2)$, and similarly for s. On the other hand, both $B_r(u)$ and $B_s(v)$ contain more than half the vertices, so they must meet. We conclude that

$$\text{diam } X \leq r + s \leq 2\log_c(n/2) + 2.$$

Chapter 3

3.7. Let S denote the generating set.

We show that $\text{diam } A_n = 2$. It suffices to consider the distance to 0. Vertices of the form $3i + 1$, where $0 \leq i \leq n - 1$, are one edge away from 0. The remaining vertices are of the form $3i$ for $1 \leq i \leq n - 1$, and $3i + 2$ for $0 \leq i \leq n - 2$. These are two edges away from 0, as $3i \sim 3i + 1$, and $3i + 2 \sim 3i + 1$.

We show that $\text{gir } A_n = 4$. An example of a 4-cycle is $0 \sim 1 \sim 8 \sim 4 \sim 0$. The lack of 3-cycles amounts to S being an independent set. To see this, take two vertices $3i + 1, 3j + 1 \in S$ where $0 \leq i \leq j \leq n - 1$; the vertices are not adjacent, as $(3j + 1) - (3i + 1) = 3(j - i) \notin S$.

We show that $\text{chr } A_n = 3$. Since $S = \{1, 4, \ldots, 3n - 2\}$ is independent, so are the translates $S + 1 = \{2, 5, \ldots, 3n - 4, 0\}$ and $S - 1 = \{0, 3, \ldots, 3n - 3\}$. Hence, three colours will do: we can assign each one of S, $S - 1$, and $(S + 1) \setminus \{0\}$ a colour. On the other hand, the presence of 5-cycles, such as $0 \sim 1 \sim 2 \sim 3 \sim 4 \sim 0$, rules out the possibility of bi-colouring.

We show that $\text{ind } A_n = n$. We already have an independent set of size n, namely S. Assume that there is some independent subset T with $n + 1$ vertices; we may furthermore assume that $0 \in T$. Then $T \setminus \{0\}$ consists of n independent vertices picked from $\{2, 5, \ldots, 3n - 4\} = (S + 1) \setminus \{0\}$ and $\{3, 6, \ldots, 3n - 3\} = (S - 1) \setminus \{0\}$. But this is impossible: the two latter sets have $n - 1$ elements each, forming $n - 1$ pairs of adjacent vertices: $2 \sim 3, 5 \sim 6, \ldots, 3n - 4 \sim 3n - 3$.

3.9. In the proof of Theorem 2.7, we saw that a logarithmic lower bound for the diameter comes from an exponential upper bound on the growth of balls around a vertex. So let us consider the growth of balls around a fixed vertex u in our Cayley graph.

Let $S = \{s_1, \ldots, s_d\}$ be the symmetric generating set for the underlying abelian group. Then every vertex in a ball of radius r around u can be written, possibly in more than one way, as $us_1^{n_1} \ldots s_d^{n_d}$, where $n_1, \ldots, n_d$ are non-negative integers satisfying $n_1 + \cdots + n_d \leq r$. There are at most $(r+1)^d$ such representations, so $|B_r(u)| \leq (r+1)^d$. For $r = \operatorname{diam} X$, this polynomial bound says that $n \leq (\operatorname{diam} X + 1)^d$. In other words, $\operatorname{diam} X \geq n^{1/d} - 1$.

3.24. Let us write G for $(\mathbb{Z}_2)^n$, and $x \cdot y$ for $x_1 y_1 + \cdots + x_n y_n$. Thus S and S' are subsets of $G \times G$ given by

$$S = \{(x, y) : x \cdot y = 1\}, \qquad S' = \{(x, y) : (x + e_1) \cdot (y + e_1) = 0\}.$$

Note that S and S' are symmetric; in fact any subset of $G \times G$ is, and they do not contain the identity $(0, 0)$. Let us check that S and S' generate $G \times G$. It suffices to generate $G \times \{0\}$; by symmetry, one can also generate $\{0\} \times G$, and so $G \times G$ as well. Given $a \in G$, we look for a decomposition $(a, 0) = (x, y) + (a + x, y)$; this is suggested by strong regularity with positive parameters. In order to have $(x, y), (a + x, y) \in S$, pick a non-zero $y \in G$ satisfying $a \cdot y = 0$, and then $x \in G$ with $x \cdot y = 1$. In order to have $(x, y), (a + x, y) \in S'$, simply take $x = 0$ and $y = e_1$.

The size of $G \times G$, the vertex set for both Cayley graphs, is m^2. Let us check that $|S| = \frac{1}{2}(m^2 - m)$. Consider the function $(x, y) \mapsto (-1)^{x \cdot y}$ on $G \times G$. It evaluates to -1 on S, respectively to 1 off S, so the characteristic function of S is given by $\mathbb{1}_S(x, y) = \frac{1}{2}(1 - (-1)^{x \cdot y})$. Now

$$|S| = \sum_{x, y \in G} \frac{1}{2}(1 - (-1)^{x \cdot y}) = \frac{1}{2}\left(m^2 - \sum_{x, y \in G} (-1)^{x \cdot y}\right)$$

and

$$\sum_{x, y \in G} (-1)^{x \cdot y} = \left(\sum_{s, t \in \mathbb{Z}_2} (-1)^{st}\right)^n = 2^n = m, \qquad (12.7)$$

yielding the desired count.

For strong regularity, we need to check that $(0, 0)$ and any other vertex $(a, b) \neq (0, 0)$ have $\frac{1}{4}(m^2 - 2m)$ common neighbours. The set of common neighbours is $S \cap ((a, b) + S)$, whose characteristic function is $(x, y) \mapsto \mathbb{1}_S(x, y)\mathbb{1}_S(a + x, b + y)$. Therefore

$$|S \cap ((a, b) + S)| = \sum_{x, y \in G} \frac{1}{4}(1 - (-1)^{x \cdot y})(1 - (-1)^{(a+x) \cdot (b+y)})$$

$$= \frac{1}{4}\left(m^2 - m - m + (-1)^{a \cdot b} \sum_{x, y \in G} (-1)^{a \cdot y + b \cdot x}\right)$$

thanks to (12.7). We are left with showing that the inner sum

$$\sum_{x, y \in G} (-1)^{a \cdot y + b \cdot x} = \left(\sum_{x \in G} (-1)^{b \cdot x}\right)\left(\sum_{y \in G} (-1)^{a \cdot y}\right)$$

vanishes. Recall that $(a, b) \neq (0, 0)$ so, without loss of generality, $a \neq 0$. Then

$$\sum_{y \in G} (-1)^{a \cdot y} = \prod_{k=1}^{n} \left(\sum_{t \in \mathbb{Z}_2} (-1)^{a_k t} \right)$$

and we note that, on the right-hand side, the factor corresponding to some $a_k \neq 0$ equals 0. So the left-hand sum vanishes, as desired.

Now let us turn to the other generating set, S'. Noting that $S' = (e_1, e_1) + S^c$, we aim to deduce the desired properties of S' from those already established for S. Firstly, $|S'| = |S^c| = m^2 - \frac{1}{2}(m^2 - m) = \frac{1}{2}(m^2 + m)$. Secondly, for each $(a, b) \neq (0, 0)$ we have

$$\begin{aligned}
\left| S' \cap ((a, b) + S') \right| &= \left| S^c \cap ((a, b) + S^c) \right| = m^2 - \left| S \cup ((a, b) + S) \right| \\
&= m^2 - 2|S| + \left| S \cap ((a, b) + S) \right| \\
&= m^2 - (m^2 - m) + \tfrac{1}{4}(m^2 - 2m) = \tfrac{1}{4}(m^2 + 2m).
\end{aligned}$$

3.26. Consider a d-regular graph having girth 6. Let S_1, S_2, and S_3 be the set of vertices at distances 1, 2, and 3, respectively, from a fixed vertex v. Then $|S_1| = d$ and $|S_2| = d(d - 1)$ by the girth assumption. Furthermore, each vertex in S_2 has $d - 1$ neighbours in S_3. On the other hand, a vertex in S_3 has at most d neighbours in S_2. Therefore $|S_3| \geq (d-1)^2$. So there are at least $1 + d + d(d-1) + (d-1)^2 = 2(d^2 - d + 1)$ vertices.

Now let us assume that a d-regular graph of girth 6 has exactly $2(d^2 - d + 1)$ vertices. As there are no further vertices beyond S_3, and v is arbitrary, it follows that the diameter is at most 3. On the other hand, the inequality $\text{gir} \leq 2 \, \text{diam}$ says that the diameter is at least 3. Thus, the diameter is 3. Furthermore, vertices in S_3 have all their neighbours in S_2. Since no two distinct vertices on a sphere are adjacent, we get a bipartite structure: $\{v\} \cup S_2$ and $S_2 \cup S_3$. We conclude that we are dealing with a design graph with parameter $c = 1$.

Chapter 4

4.2. We first show that every element in $\text{GL}_n(\mathbb{F})$ has order at most $q^n - 1$. By the Cayley–Hamilton theorem, each power of $A \in \text{GL}_n(\mathbb{F})$ is a non-zero linear combination of the form $c_{n-1} A^{n-1} + \cdots + c_1 A + c_0$. So there are at most $q^n - 1$ distinct powers of A, implying that A has order at most $q^n - 1$.

Next, we show that $\text{GL}_n(\mathbb{F})$ has an element of order $q^n - 1$. Let $\mathbb{K}$ be a field with q^n elements containing $\mathbb{F}$. Viewing $\mathbb{K}$ as an n-dimensional linear space over $\mathbb{F}$, we get an isomorphism between $\mathrm{GL}_n(\mathbb{F})$ and the group of $\mathbb{F}$-linear isomorphisms of $\mathbb{K}$. Now let g be a generator of the cyclic group $\mathbb{K}^*$. Multiplication by g defines an $\mathbb{F}$-linear isomorphism of $\mathbb{K}$ of order $q^n - 1$.

4.4. Note that $\mathrm{Tr}(b^q) = \mathrm{Tr}(\phi(b)) = \phi(\mathrm{Tr}(b)) = \mathrm{Tr}(b)$, and so $\{b^q - b : b \in \mathbb{K}\} \subseteq \{a \in \mathbb{K} : \mathrm{Tr}(a) = 0\}$. We establish equality by counting. The equation $\mathrm{Tr}(a) = 0$ has at most q^{n-1} solutions in $\mathbb{K}$. On the other hand, $\{b^q - b : b \in \mathbb{K}\}$ has precisely q^{n-1} elements since $b^q - b = c^q - c$ if and only if $\phi(b - c) = b - c$, that is, $b - c \in \mathbb{F}$.

Similarly, $\mathrm{Nm}(b^q) = \mathrm{Nm}(b)$ so $\{b^q/b : b \in \mathbb{K}^*\} \subseteq \{a \in \mathbb{K} : \mathrm{Nm}(a) = 1\}$. The right-hand set has at most $(q^n - 1)/(q - 1)$ elements. The left-hand set has precisely $(q^n - 1)/(q - 1)$ elements: for $b, c \in \mathbb{K}^*$ we have $b^q/b = c^q/c$ if and only if $\phi(b/c) = b/c$, that is, $b/c \in \mathbb{F}^*$.

4.7. A direct summand of the given k-space, say W, is an $(n - k)$-space. There are $(q^n - q^k)(q^n - q^{k+1}) \cdots (q^n - q^{n-1})$ ordered ways of choosing $n - k$ linearly independent vectors that lie outside W. On the other hand, an $(n - k)$-space has $(q^{n-k} - 1) \cdots (q^{n-k} - q^{n-k-1})$ ordered bases. Dividing out and cancelling, we find that there are $q^{k(n-k)}$ direct summands for W.

4.16. This is just a rephrasing of previous ideas. The incidence graph $I_3(q)$ is (isomorphic to) the bi-Cayley graph of the cyclic group $\mathbb{Z}_{q^2+q+1}$ with respect to a certain subset S of size $q + 1$. The vertices are a black copy and a white copy of $\mathbb{Z}_{q^2+q+1}$. The white 0 is adjacent to black elements from S, and every other white vertex is incident to precisely one of these black S-vertices. This means that the $(q+1)q = q^2 + q$ distinct differences $\{s_1 - s_2 : s_1 \neq s_2 \in S\}$ parameterize, in a unique way, the non-zero elements of $\mathbb{Z}_{q^2+q+1}$.

Chapter 5

5.6. Let $N_n(c)$ denote the number of solutions to the equation $X_1^2 + \cdots + X_n^2 = c$. Then we have the relation

$$N_{n+1}(c) = \sum_{a+b=c} N_n(a)N_1(b).$$

This reads like a recurrence relation for N_n. Note, however, that the coefficients $N_1(b) = 1 + \sigma(b)$ are essentially alternating between 0 and 2. This motivates us to consider the 2-step recurrence relation

$$N_{n+2}(c) = \sum_{a+b=c} N_n(a)N_2(b).$$

Now the coefficients $N_2(b)$ are essentially constant, namely, $N_2(b) = q - \sigma(-1)$ for $b \neq 0$. Henceforth, we use the shorthand $\sigma(-1) = \epsilon$. The above recurrence relation becomes

$$N_{n+2}(c) = N_2(0)N_n(c) + (q - \epsilon) \sum_{a \neq c} N_n(a).$$

The relation $\sum_b N_2(b) = q^2$ yields $N_2(0) = q + \epsilon(q - 1)$. Similarly, we have $\sum_{a \neq c} N_n(a) = q^n - N_n(c)$. Therefore

$$N_{n+2}(c) = \big(q + \epsilon(q - 1)\big)N_n(c) + (q - \epsilon)\big(q^n - N_n(c)\big)$$
$$= q^{n+1} - \epsilon q^n + \epsilon q N_n(c).$$

In other words,

$$N_n(c) = q^{n-1} + r_n(c),$$

where the remainder satisfies the simple recurrence $r_{n+2}(c) = (\epsilon q)r_n(c)$. The initial values $r_1(c)$ and $r_2(c)$ can be easily found: $N_1(c) = 1 + r_1(c)$ equals $1 + \sigma(c)$, and $N_2(c) = q + r_2(c)$ equals $q - \epsilon$ for $c \neq 0$, respectively $q + \epsilon(q - 1)$ for $c = 0$. We conclude that the remainder $r_n(c)$ can be tabulated, according to the parity of n, as follows.

	$n = 2k + 1$	$n = 2k$
$c \neq 0$	$\sigma(c)\epsilon^k q^k$	$-\epsilon^k q^{k-1}$
$c = 0$	0	$\epsilon^k(q - 1)q^{k-1}$

5.9. By Exercise 5.6, we have

$$N = p^{\ell-1} + (p^*)^{(\ell-1)/2},$$

where, we recall, $p^* = (-1/p)p$. Now $p^{\ell-1} \equiv 1 \bmod \ell$ by Fermat's little theorem, and $(p^*)^{(\ell-1)/2} \equiv (p^*/\ell) \bmod \ell$ by Euler's formula in $\mathbb{Z}_\ell$. Thus $N \equiv 1 + (p^*/\ell) \bmod \ell$.

If $(x_1, \ldots, x_\ell)$ is a solution to the equation $X_1^2 + \cdots + X_\ell^2 = 1$, then so is the cyclic permutation $(x_\ell, x_1, \ldots, x_{\ell-1})$. Iterating, we see that $(x_1, \ldots, x_\ell)$ comes in a pack of ℓ solutions, except when $x_1 = x_2 = \cdots = x_\ell$. Thus $N \bmod \ell$ equals the number of solutions to the equation $\ell X^2 = 1$, which is $1 + (\ell/p)$.

Therefore $(\ell/p) \equiv (p^*/\ell) \bmod \ell$, and so $(\ell/p) = (p^*/\ell)$.

5.11. As the context suggests, we show that the Paley graph $P(17)$ has no complete subgraph on 4 vertices. By 'switching', that is, scaling by a non-square, we also see that $P(17)$ has no independent subset of 4 vertices. Therefore $R(4) > 17$.

Assume, by way of contradiction, that there is a complete subgraph with distinct vertices x, y, z, t in $P(17)$. By translating, we may assume that $t = 0$. Then z is a non-zero square, and scaling by its inverse allows us to assume that $z = 1$. Now $x \neq 1$

has the property that both x and $x - 1$ are squares, and the same holds for $y \neq 1$. The squares in $\mathbb{Z}_{17}$ are $\{\pm 1, \pm 2, \pm 4, \pm 8\}$, and a quick analysis reduces the possibilities for x and y to $\{2, -1, -8\}$. The difference $x - y$ is then one of $\{\pm 3, \pm 7\}$. Since none is a square, we have reached a contradiction.

5.15. A bi-Cayley graph isomorphism is a group isomorphism mapping one connecting set onto the other. Obviously, such an algebraic isomorphism gives rise to a graph-theoretic isomorphism between the corresponding bi-Cayley graphs.

By definition, $BP(7)$ is the bi-Cayley graph of the additive group $\mathbb{Z}_7$ with respect to the non-zero multiplicative squares, $\{1, 2, 4\}$. On the other hand, we view $I_3(2)$ as the bi-Cayley graph of the multiplicative group $\mathbb{F}_8^*$ with respect to the zero-trace set, $\{s : \text{Tr}(s) = 0\}$, where $\text{Tr} : \mathbb{F}_8 \to \mathbb{F}_2$. We look for a group isomorphism between the cyclic groups $\mathbb{F}_8^*$ and $\mathbb{Z}_7$, mapping $\{s : \text{Tr}(s) = 0\}$ to $\{1, 2, 4\}$. To that end, we need a concrete picture of the field $\mathbb{F}_8$.

There are two irreducible polynomials of degree 3 over $\mathbb{F}_2$, $X^3 + X + 1$ and $X^3 + X^2 + 1$. The first one turns out to be slightly more convenient, as it leads to simpler-looking computations. So we model $\mathbb{F}_8$ as

$$\mathbb{F}_2[X]/(X^3 + X + 1) = \{a + b\alpha + c\alpha^2 : a, b, c \in \mathbb{F}_2, \ \alpha^3 = \alpha + 1\}.$$

Now

$$\begin{aligned} \text{Tr}(a + b\alpha + c\alpha^2) &= (a + b\alpha + c\alpha^2) + (a + b\alpha + c\alpha^2)^2 + (a + b\alpha + c\alpha^2)^4 \\ &= (a + b\alpha + c\alpha^2) + (a + b\alpha^2 + c\alpha^4) + (a + b\alpha^4 + c\alpha^8) \\ &= a + (b + c)(\alpha + \alpha^2 + \alpha^4) = a, \end{aligned}$$

as $\alpha^8 = \alpha$, and $\alpha + \alpha^2 + \alpha^4 = 0$ by the defining relation for α. Thus $\{s : \text{Tr}(s) = 0\} = \{\alpha, \alpha^2, \alpha + \alpha^2 = \alpha^4\}$. At this point we hope that α is a generator for $\mathbb{F}_8^*$, and this turns out to be the case indeed. We conclude that $\alpha \mapsto 1$ defines a group isomorphism $\mathbb{F}_8^* \to \mathbb{Z}_7$, sending $\{s : \text{Tr}(s) = 0\}$ to $\{1, 2, 4\}$.

Chapter 6

6.9. Up to replacing d by $\gcd(d, |G|)$, we may assume that d divides $|G|$. Consider the case when $\{h \in G : h^d = g\}$ is non-empty. Then $\chi(g) = 1$ whenever $\chi^d = 1$, so

$$\sum_{\chi^d = 1} \chi(g) = \left|\{\chi \in G^\wedge : \chi^d = 1\}\right| = \left|\{h \in G : h^d = 1\}\right| = \left|\{h \in G : h^d = g\}\right|.$$

Now consider the case when $\{h \in G : h^d = g\}$ is empty, that is, $g \notin G^d$. We claim that there is a character χ' satisfying $(\chi')^d = 1$, and $\chi'(g) \neq 1$. Indeed, as

$[g] \in G/G^d$ is non-trivial, there is a character μ of G/G^d with $\mu([g]) \neq 1$. Let χ' be the lift of μ via the quotient map $G \to G/G^d$. Then $\chi'(g) = \mu([g]) \neq 1$, and $(\chi')^d = 1$ as $\chi' = 1$ on G^d. Using χ', the same trick as in Corollary 6.7 shows that $\sum_{\chi^d=1} \chi(g) = 0$.

6.11. (i) Assume that $\chi_1\chi_2$ is non-trivial. As in the proof of Theorem 6.10, we expand and rearrange the product

$$G(\psi, \chi_1)G(\psi, \chi_2) = \sum_{s,t \in \mathbb{F}} \psi(s)\psi(t)\chi_1(s)\chi_2(t) = \sum_{s,t \in \mathbb{F}} \psi(s+t)\chi_1(s)\chi_2(t)$$

$$= \sum_{s \in \mathbb{F}} \chi_1(s) \sum_{t \in \mathbb{F}} \psi(s+t)\chi_2(t) = \sum_{s \in \mathbb{F}} \chi_1(s) \sum_{t \in \mathbb{F}} \psi(t)\chi_2(t-s)$$

$$= \sum_{t \in \mathbb{F}} \psi(t) \sum_{s \in \mathbb{F}} \chi_1(s)\chi_2(t-s).$$

When $t = 0$, the inner sum is

$$\sum_{s \in \mathbb{F}} \chi_1(s)\chi_2(-s) = \chi_2(-1) \sum_{s \in \mathbb{F}} (\chi_1\chi_2)(s) = 0.$$

When $t \neq 0$, after the change of variable $s \mapsto ts$ the inner sum becomes

$$\sum_{s \in \mathbb{F}} \chi_1(ts)\chi_2(t(1-s)) = (\chi_1\chi_2)(t)J(\chi_1, \chi_2).$$

Thus

$$G(\psi, \chi_1)G(\psi, \chi_2) = J(\chi_1, \chi_2) \sum_{t \in \mathbb{F}^*} \psi(t)(\chi_1\chi_2)(t) = J(\chi_1, \chi_2)G(\psi, \chi_1\chi_2).$$

We deduce that $|J(\chi_1, \chi_2)| = \sqrt{q}$ by taking absolute values in the above relation, and using Theorem 6.10.

The computation of $J(\chi, \chi^{-1})$ for non-trivial χ runs as in the proof of Lemma 5.4. We have

$$J(\chi, \chi^{-1}) = \sum_{s+t=1} \chi(s)\chi^{-1}(t) = \sum_{t \neq} \chi(1-t)\chi(t^{-1}) = \sum_{t \neq 0} \chi(t^{-1} - 1).$$

The map $t \mapsto t^{-1} - 1$ is a bijection from $\mathbb{F}^*$ to $\mathbb{F} \setminus \{-1\}$, so the latter sum equals $-\chi(-1)$. We conclude that $J(\chi, \chi^{-1}) = -\chi(-1) = \pm 1$.

(ii) If $q \equiv 1 \bmod 4$, then there exists a multiplicative character χ having order 4. On the one hand, $|J(\chi, \chi)|^2 = q$ as $\chi^2 \neq 1$. On the other hand, χ takes values in $\{\pm 1, \pm i, 0\}$ so $J(\chi, \chi)$ is a Gaussian integer $a + bi$ for some $a, b \in \mathbb{Z}$. Thus $|J(\chi, \chi)|^2 = a^2 + b^2$, and we conclude that $q = a^2 + b^2$.

6.16. (i) Using Exercise 6.9, we have

$$\sum_{\chi^d=1} G(\psi,\chi) = \sum_{t\in\mathbb{F}^*}\psi(t)\sum_{\chi^d=1}\chi(t) = \sum_{t\in\mathbb{F}^*}\psi(t)\left|\{s\in\mathbb{F}^* : s^d = t\}\right| = \sum_{s\in\mathbb{F}^*}\psi(s^d).$$

As $G(\psi,\mathbb{1}) = -1 = -\psi(0)$, we obtain

$$\sum_{s\in\mathbb{F}}\psi(s^d) = \sum_{\chi^d=\mathbb{1},\chi\neq\mathbb{1}} G(\psi,\chi).$$

There are at most $d-1$ terms on the right-hand side, each of absolute value $\sqrt{q}$. The claimed bound follows.

(ii) Recall, $\{s^{q-1} : s \in \mathbb{K}^*\}$ is a $(q-1)$-to-1 parameterization of $\{s \in \mathbb{K}^* :$ $\mathrm{Nm}(s) = 1\}$. Thus

$$S(\psi) = \sum_{\mathrm{Nm}(s)=1}\psi(s) = \frac{1}{q-1}\sum_{s\in\mathbb{K}^*}\psi(s^{q-1}).$$

By part (i) the latter sum has absolute value at most $(q-2)q^{n/2} + 1$. Hence

$$|S(\psi)| \le \frac{(q-2)q^{n/2}+1}{q-1} < q^{n/2}.$$

Chapter 7

7.4. A graph on n vertices is regular if and only if

$$n\left(\sum \deg(v)^2\right) = \left(\sum \deg(v)\right)^2.$$

Firstly, $L(v,v) = \deg(v)$ so

$$\sum \deg(v) = \mathrm{Tr}\, L = \sum \lambda_k.$$

Secondly, one computes that $L^2(v,v) = \deg(v)^2 + \deg(v)$. Therefore

$$\sum \deg(v)^2 = \mathrm{Tr}\, L^2 - \mathrm{Tr}\, L = \sum \lambda_k^2 - \sum \lambda_k.$$

In conclusion, a graph is regular if and only if its Laplacian spectrum satisfies the relation

$$n\left(\sum \lambda_k^2\right) = \left(\sum \lambda_k\right)^2 + n\sum \lambda_k.$$

7.12. (i) The two Laplacians, L for X and L' for the complement of X, are related by $L + L' = nI - J$. If λ is an eigenvalue of L with eigenfunction f, then $L'f = (n - \lambda)f - Jf$, where $Jf = 0$ whenever f is orthogonal to $\mathbb{1}$. Firstly, if $\lambda \neq 0$ then L' has eigenvalue $n - \lambda$ with multiplicity equal to the multiplicity of λ. Secondly, consider the eigenvalue $\lambda = 0$. Taking an orthogonal basis $f_1 = \mathbb{1}, f_2, \ldots, f_{m(0)}$ for its eigenspace, we obtain that L' has eigenvalues 0, and n with multiplicity $m(0) - 1$. A multiplicity count shows that all eigenvalues of L' are accounted for.

(ii) The complement of $K_{n_1,\ldots,n_k}$ is the disconnected union of the complete graphs $K_{n_1}, \ldots, K_{n_k}$. So its Laplacian spectrum is 0 with multiplicity k, and n_j with multiplicity $n_j - 1$ for $j = 1, \ldots, k$. In light of part (i), the Laplacian spectrum of $K_{n_1,\ldots,n_k}$ is 0 with multiplicity 1; n with multiplicity $k - 1$; $n - n_j$ with multiplicity $n_j - 1$ for $j = 1, \ldots, k$. Here $n = n_1 + \cdots + n_k$ is, as usual, the number of vertices.

7.13. (i) On the cone, the eigenrelations describing a Laplacian eigenvalue are

$$\lambda' g_* = n g_* - \sum_v g(v), \quad \lambda' g(v) = g(v) + Lg(v) - g_*, \tag{12.8}$$

where all the ingredients, except for the value g_* at the apex, are relative to the base graph X.

Let $0, \lambda_2, \ldots, \lambda_n$ be the Laplacian spectrum of X, and let $\mathbb{1}, g_2, \ldots, g_n$ be an orthogonal basis of Laplacian eigenvectors. Extend each g_k to the cone by setting $g_* = 0$. The first relation in (12.8) is satisfied, for any λ', since $\sum_v g_k(v) = 0$. The second is satisfied with $\lambda' = \lambda_k + 1$. To extend the constant eigenvector $\mathbb{1}$ to an eigenvector for the cone, we seek to satisfy $\lambda' g_* = n g_* - n$, $\lambda' = 1 - g_*$. The possibilities are $\lambda' = 0$ with $g_* = 1$, and $\lambda' = n + 1$ with $g_* = -n$. As the Laplacian eigenvectors for the cone that we have obtained are linearly independent, there are no further Laplacian eigenvalues. We conclude that the Laplacian spectrum of the cone is $0, \lambda_2 + 1, \ldots, \lambda_n + 1, n + 1$.

(ii) Assuming that the base X is regular, the adjacency eigenrelations on the cone are

$$\alpha' f_* = \sum f(v), \quad \alpha' f(v) = Af(v) + f_*. \tag{12.9}$$

Let $d, \alpha_2, \ldots, \alpha_n$ be the adjacency spectrum of X, and let $\mathbb{1}, f_2, \ldots, f_n$ be a corresponding orthogonal basis of eigenvectors. Extend each f_k by setting $f_* = 0$. Then (12.9) holds with $\alpha' = \alpha_k$. The extension for $\mathbb{1}$ is determined by $\alpha' f_* = n$ and $\alpha' = d + f_*$, that is, $f_* = \alpha' - d$, where α' satisfies $\alpha'(\alpha' - d) = n$. Again, there cannot be any further adjacency eigenvalues for the cone, so its adjacency spectrum is $\alpha_2, \ldots, \alpha_n, \frac{1}{2}(d \pm \sqrt{d^2 + 4n})$.

(iii) A star with n pendant vertices is the cone over n singletons. Its Laplacian eigenvalues are 0, 1 (with multiplicity $n - 1$), and $n + 1$. Its adjacency eigenvalues are 0 (with multiplicity $n - 1$), and $\pm\sqrt{n}$.

A windmill graph with n blades is the cone over the disconnected union of n copies of K_2. Its Laplacian eigenvalues are 0, 1 (with multiplicity $n - 1$), 3 (with multiplicity n), and $2n + 1$. Its adjacency eigenvalues are 1 (with multiplicity $n - 1$), -1 (with multiplicity n), and $\frac{1}{2}(1 \pm \sqrt{1 + 8n})$.

Consider a wheel graph Wh_n with n spokes, viewed as the cone over the cycle graph C_n. As for any cone over a non-complete base, Wh_n has diameter 2 for $n \geq 4$. The base has $\lfloor n/2 \rfloor + 1$ distinct eigenvalues of each kind. Part (i) shows that the number of distinct Laplacian eigenvalues does not decrease by coning, and it increases by 1 if the base has $\lambda_{max} < n$. As $\lambda_{max}(C_n) \leq 4$, we deduce that Wh_n has $\lfloor n/2 \rfloor + 2$ distinct Laplacian eigenvalues for $n \geq 5$. Part (ii) tells us that the number of distinct adjacency eigenvalues does not decrease by coning a d-regular base, since $\alpha_2 \leq d < \frac{1}{2}(d + \sqrt{d^2 + 4n})$. Furthermore, the number increases by 1 if the base satisfies $n > 2d^2$, for then $\alpha_{min} \geq -d > \frac{1}{2}(d - \sqrt{d^2 + 4n})$. We deduce that Wh_n has $\lfloor n/2 \rfloor + 2$ distinct adjacency eigenvalues for $n \geq 9$.

Chapter 8

8.5. The halved cube graph $\frac{1}{2}Q_n$ is the Cayley graph of $G = \{v \in (\mathbb{Z}_2)^n : \sum v_i = 0\}$ with respect to $S = \{e_i + e_j : 1 \leq i < j \leq n\}$. Being a subgroup of $(\mathbb{Z}_2)^n$, G inherits the characters $\chi_I(v) = (-1)^{\sum_{i \in I} v_i}$ for $I \subseteq \{1, \ldots, n\}$. Note, however, that complementary sets define the same character over G, and we write $\chi_{\{I,I^c\}}$ for the character of G obtained by restricting $\chi_I = \chi_{I^c}$. Now

$$\chi_{\{I,I^c\}}(e_i + e_j) = \begin{cases} -1 & \text{if } \{I, I^c\} \text{ separates } i \text{ from } j, \\ 1 & \text{if } \{I, I^c\} \text{ does not separate } i \text{ from } j. \end{cases}$$

One easily sees that different partitions define different characters of G. Thus there are $2^{n-1} = |G|$ characters of G of the form $\chi_{\{I,I^c\}}$, so we have all the characters of G.

The adjacency eigenvalue corresponding to a character $\chi_{\{I,I^c\}}$ is

$$\alpha_{\{I,I^c\}} = \sum_{i<j} \chi_{\{I,I^c\}}(e_i + e_j)$$

$$= \#(\text{2-subsets}) - 2 \cdot \#(\text{2-subsets separated by } \{I, I^c\}) = \binom{n}{2} - 2|I||I^c|,$$

with multiplicity $\binom{n}{|I|} = \binom{n}{|I^c|}$. The degree being $\binom{n}{2}$, we conclude that the Laplacian eigenvalues are $2k(n - k)$ for $k = 0, \ldots, \lfloor n/2 \rfloor$.

8.6. The trivial adjacency eigenvalue is the degree, n. Let us find the non-trivial ones. The non-trivial characters of $\mathbb{Z}_{3n-1}$ are defined by $\psi(1) = \zeta$, where $\zeta \neq 1$ runs over the roots of unity of order $3n - 1$. To compute the eigenvalue $\alpha_\psi = \sum_{s \in S} \psi(s)$, we make the following observation: S together with the translates $S + 1$ and $S + 2$ tile $\mathbb{Z}_{3n-1}$, except that 1 is covered twice. The fundamental relation, that ψ has zero sum over $\mathbb{Z}_{3n-1}$, becomes

$$\zeta = \sum_{s \in S} \psi(s) + \sum_{s \in S} \psi(s + 1) + \sum_{s \in S} \psi(s + 2) = \alpha_\psi + \zeta \alpha_\psi + \zeta^2 \alpha_\psi,$$

and so

$$\alpha_\psi = \frac{\zeta}{1 + \zeta + \zeta^2} = \frac{1}{1 + \zeta + \bar{\zeta}} = \frac{1}{1 + 2\,\mathrm{Re}(\zeta)}.$$

Note that ζ and $\bar{\zeta}$ yield the same eigenvalue. There are $\lfloor (3n - 1)/2 \rfloor + 1$ distinct adjacency eigenvalues. On the other hand, we know that A_n has diameter 2.

8.7. Part (i) is a direct verification, left to the reader; let us turn to part (ii). The characters of the additive group $\mathbb{F}^n$ are $\{\chi_a : a \in \mathbb{F}^n\}$. The corresponding adjacency eigenvalues are

$$\alpha_a = \sum_{s,t \in \mathbb{F}^*} \chi_a(s, st, \dots, st^{n-1}) = \sum_{s,t \in \mathbb{F}^*} \chi\big(s(a_1 + a_2 t + \cdots + a_n t^{n-1})\big).$$

Let P_a denote the polynomial $a_1 + a_2 X + \cdots + a_n X^{n-1}$. If $t \neq 0$ is a root of P_a, then

$$\sum_{s \in \mathbb{F}^*} \chi\big(sP_a(t)\big) = \sum_{s \in \mathbb{F}^*} \chi(0) = q - 1.$$

If $t \neq 0$ is not a root of P_a, then

$$\sum_{s \in \mathbb{F}^*} \chi\big(sP_a(t)\big) = \sum_{s \in \mathbb{F}^*} \chi(s) = -1.$$

Thus, if n_a denotes the number of non-zero roots of P_a, then

$$\alpha_a = (q - 1)n_a + (-1)(q - 1 - n_a) = q(n_a - 1) + 1.$$

The smallest possible value of n_a is 0, achieved when, say, $P_a = X^{n-1}$. So $\alpha_{\min} = -(q - 1)$. The largest possible value of n_a is $q - 1$, achieved for $a = 0$, and this yields the trivial eigenvalue $\alpha_{\max} = (q - 1)^2$. Consider now the case when $a \neq 0$. Then $n_a \leq n - 1$, as P_a has at most $n - 1$ roots, and $n_a \leq q - 1$. Thus $n_a \leq \min\{n, q\} - 1$. If $n < q$, then $n_a = n - 1$ is achieved by $P_a = (X - t_1) \dots (X - t_{n-1})$, where $t_1, \dots, t_{n-1} \neq 0$ are distinct. If $n \geq q$, then $n_a = q - 1$ is achieved by $P_a = X^{n-q} \prod_{t \neq 0}(X - t)$.

   We conclude that the second largest eigenvalue is $q(\min\{q, n\} - 2) + 1$, and that the graph is connected (i.e., S is generating) if and only if $n < q$.

8.17. Consider a graph, say X, whose bipartite double is a design graph with parameters (m, d, c). Then X is a d-regular graph of size m, with the property that any two distinct vertices have c common neighbours. So X is either a complete graph, or a strongly regular graph with equal parameters, $a = c$. The first case means that $(m, d, c) = (m, m - 1, m - 2)$, which is not the case for $I_n(q)$. So the second case must hold. Then X is of integral type. Let $t^2 = \text{disc} = 4(d - c)$, where t divides $2d$. Putting $t = 2t'$, we get that $t'^2 = d - c$ and t' divides d. But then t' divides c as well. Summarizing, $d - c$ is the square of a common divisor of d and c.

   The incidence graph $I_n(q)$ is a design graph with

$$d = \frac{q^{n-1} - 1}{q - 1}, \qquad c = \frac{q^{n-2} - 1}{q - 1}.$$

The relation $d = qc + 1$ implies that d and c are relatively prime. Now the condition of the previous paragraph forces $d - c = 1$, a contradiction.

8.25. The incidence graph, let us call it X, is a partial design graph with parameters

$$m = \binom{n}{2}_q, \quad d = \binom{n-2}{2}_q, \quad c_1 = \binom{n-3}{2}_q, \quad c_2 = \binom{n-4}{2}_q.$$

The half-size m, and the degree d, are clear. So let us justify the joint parameters, c_1 and c_2. Given two $(n - 2)$-spaces, their common neighbours are the 2-spaces contained in their intersection. The sum of two distinct $(n - 2)$-spaces has dimension $n - 1$ or n, so their intersection has dimension $n - 3$ or $n - 4$. The number of 2-spaces contained in an $(n - 3)$-space, respectively in an $(n - 4)$-space, is given by the q-binomial coefficient c_1, respectively c_2. Consider now the other side of the bipartition. Given two 2-spaces, their common neighbours are the $(n - 2)$-spaces containing their sum. The sum of two distinct 2-spaces is a 3-space or a 4-space, according to whether the two 2-spaces intersect in a 1-space or the 0-space. The q-binomial coefficients c_1 and c_2 count the number of $(n - 2)$-spaces containing a given 3-space or a given 4-space.

   The associated c_1-graph X' has the 2-spaces ('planes') as its vertices, and edges connect those that intersect in a 1-space ('line'). The graph X' is regular of degree $d' = (q + 1)k$, where

$$k = \binom{n-1}{1}_q - 1 = \frac{q^{n-1} - q}{q - 1},$$

for there are $q + 1$ lines in a fixed plane P, and k planes different from P that contain a given line of P. Furthermore, X' is strongly regular with parameters

$$a' = k - 1 + q^2, \quad c' = (q + 1)^2.$$

Indeed, consider two planes P and P'. If they do not share a line, then their common neighbours are the planes spanned by a line in P and a line in P'. There are $(q + 1)^2$ such planes. If P and P' share a line L, then their common neighbours are of two types. Firstly, the planes different from P and P' that contain L; there are $k - 1$ such planes. Secondly, the planes spanned by a line different from L in P, and a line different from L in P'; there are q^2 such planes.

The non-trivial adjacency eigenvalues of X' are easily computed, from the relations $\alpha_2' + \alpha_3' = a' - c'$, $\alpha_2'\alpha_3' = c' - d'$, to be $\alpha_2' = k - (q + 1)$ and $\alpha_3' = -(q + 1)$. Computations involving the parameters of X are more daunting, so let us spell them out. We need to compute $(d - c_2) + (c_1 - c_2)\alpha'$. Using the Pascal recurrence formulas, we have

$$c_1 - c_2 = \binom{n - 3}{2}_q - \binom{n - 4}{2}_q = q^{n-5}\binom{n - 4}{1}_q,$$

respectively

$$d - c_1 = \binom{n - 2}{2}_q - \binom{n - 3}{2}_q = q^{n-4}\binom{n - 3}{1}_q.$$

For $\alpha_3' = -(q + 1)$ we get

$$(d - c_2) - (c_1 - c_2)(q + 1) = (d - c_1) - (c_1 - c_2)q$$
$$= q^{n-4}\left(\binom{n - 3}{1}_q - \binom{n - 4}{1}_q\right) = q^{2n-8}.$$

For $\alpha_2' = k - (q + 1)$ we get

$$(d - c_2) - (c_1 - c_2)(q + 1) + (c_1 - c_2)k = q^{2n-8} + q^{n-4}\frac{(q^{n-4} - 1)(q^{n-2} - 1)}{(q - 1)^2}$$
$$= q^{n-4}\frac{(q^{n-3} - 1)^2}{(q - 1)^2}.$$

To summarize, the adjacency eigenvalues of X are

$$\pm\frac{(q^{n-2} - 1)(q^{n-3} - 1)}{(q^2 - 1)(q - 1)}, \qquad \pm\frac{q^{(n-4)/2}(q^{n-3} - 1)}{(q - 1)}, \qquad \pm q^{n-4},$$

that is, roughly $\pm q^{2(n-4)}$, $\pm q^{3(n-4)/2}$, $\pm q^{n-4}$.

Chapter 9

9.8. We put aside the largest eigenvalue $\alpha_{\max} = \alpha_1$. By the Cauchy–Schwarz inequality, we have

$$\left(\sum_{k \geq 2} |\alpha_k|\right)^2 \leq (n-1) \sum_{k \geq 2} \alpha_k^2,$$

and so, using $\sum \alpha_k^2 = nd_{\text{ave}}$, we get

$$\sum |\alpha_k| \leq \alpha_{\max} + \sqrt{(n-1)(nd_{\text{ave}} - \alpha_{\max}^2)}.$$

Elementary calculus shows that the function $f(x) = x + \sqrt{(n-1)(nd_{\text{ave}} - x^2)}$, defined over the interval $\left[0, \sqrt{nd_{\text{ave}}}\right]$, is decreasing as long as $x^2 \geq d_{\text{ave}}$. Recall that $\alpha_{\max} \geq d_{\text{ave}}$, in particular $\alpha_{\max}^2 \geq d_{\text{ave}}$ since $d_{\text{ave}} \geq 1$. Therefore

$$\sum |\alpha_k| \leq d_{\text{ave}} + \sqrt{(n-1)(nd_{\text{ave}} - d_{\text{ave}}^2)}.$$

The last step is to find the maximum of the function $g(x) = x + \sqrt{(n-1)(nx - x^2)}$ over the interval $[0, n]$. By elementary calculus, once again, the maximum is $\frac{1}{2}n(\sqrt{n} + 1)$, uniquely attained at $x = \frac{1}{2}(n + \sqrt{n})$. Thus

$$\sum |\alpha_k| \leq \tfrac{1}{2}n(\sqrt{n} + 1),$$

as desired.

Equality is achieved if and only if the following hold: the non-trivial eigenvalues have equal absolute value, $\alpha_{\max} = d_{\text{ave}}$, and $d_{\text{ave}} = \frac{1}{2}(n + \sqrt{n})$. The second condition means that the graph is regular, and the third condition spells out the degree, $\frac{1}{2}(n+\sqrt{n})$. The first requirement splits into two cases. The first is that there is just one non-trivial eigenvalue, meaning that the graph is K_n, and then the degree condition forces $n = 4$. The second is that there are two non-trivial eigenvalues, of opposite signs. Then the graph is strongly regular with equal parameters, $a = c$. Thanks to the relation given by Proposition 3.20, their common value is $\frac{1}{4}(n + 2\sqrt{n})$. In summary, equality is achieved by K_4, and strongly regular graphs with parameters $(n, d, a, c) = (n, \frac{1}{2}(n + \sqrt{n}), \frac{1}{4}(n+2\sqrt{n}), \frac{1}{4}(n+2\sqrt{n}))$. Examples of such graphs appear in Exercise 3.24.

9.10. The adjacency matrix satisfies $(A - 3I)(A - I)(A + 2I) = 0$ since its eigenvalues are 3, 1, and -2. Expanding and then taking traces leads to $\text{Tr}\, A^3 = 2\,\text{Tr}\, A^2 - 6n$. In particular, $\text{Tr}\, A^2 \geq 3n$. On the other hand, $\text{Tr}\, A^2 = nd_{\text{ave}} \leq 3n$. Therefore $d_{\text{ave}} = 3$, the largest adjacency eigenvalue. We deduce that the graph is regular, of degree 3. It is in fact strongly regular, as it has three distinct eigenvalues, with $a = 0$ and $c = 1$. Now a 3-regular on 10 vertices having diameter 2 and girth 5 is the Petersen graph.

False: there are non-Petersen graphs with Laplacian eigenvalues 0, 2, 5. Such a graph has to have diameter 2, and this points to the coning construction of Exercise 7.13 as a possible source of examples. One finds that the cone over a star graph with 3 pendant vertices does the job.

9.18. A graph of maximal degree d contains a d-star, that is, a star with d pendant vertices, as a subgraph. Recalling that a d-star has $\alpha_{max} = \sqrt{d}$ and $\lambda_{max} = d + 1$, the desired bounds follow by Theorem 9.17. Furthermore, the equality $\alpha_{max} = \sqrt{d}$ implies, conversely, that the graph is a d-star.

Revisiting the Laplacian part of the proof of Theorem 9.17, we notice the following: if X' is a subgraph of X with the property that λ'_{max} has a nowhere-vanishing eigenfunction g', then $\lambda'_{max} = \lambda_{max}$ forces X' to have all the vertices of X. For a d-star, we know that the largest Laplacian eigenvalue has a nowhere vanishing eigenfunction: this can be seen directly, or by using a general principle applying to all bipartite graphs. Therefore $\lambda_{max} = d + 1$ implies that the graph is a d-star with additional edges. Such an enhanced d-star has, indeed, $\lambda_{max} = d + 1$: it contains a d-star, and it is contained in the complete graph K_{d+1}, both of which have the largest Laplacian eigenvalue equal to $d + 1$.

Chapter 10

10.2. Let u and v be non-adjacent vertices. Consider the function f which equals 1 at the vertex u, -1 at the vertex v, and 0 elsewhere. Then $\langle f, f \rangle = 2$, $\langle Lf, f \rangle = \deg(u) + \deg(v) \leq 2d$, and $\lambda_2 \langle f, f \rangle \leq \langle Lf, f \rangle$. Therefore $\lambda_2 \leq d$.

For α_2, we adapt the previous argument. Let f be a positive eigenfunction of α_{max}. Then we have the following adjacency analogue of (10.3):

$$\alpha_2 = \min_{0 \neq g \perp f} \frac{\langle Ag, g \rangle}{\langle g, g \rangle}.$$

Let u and v be non-adjacent vertices, and define g as follows: $g(u) = f(u)$, $g(v) = -f(v)$, and $g = 0$ for all the other vertices. Then $g \neq 0$ and g is orthogonal to f. Also $\langle Ag, g \rangle = 0$, so $\alpha_2 \geq 0$.

10.10. Consider the spaces V'_k and V''_ℓ associated to M' and M'', as well as the $(k + \ell)$-dimensional space $V = V'_k \oplus V''_\ell$. Then $\mu_{k+\ell} \leq \max_{f \in V} R(f)$. Given a non-zero $f \in V$, we write

$$f = \begin{pmatrix} af' \\ bf'' \end{pmatrix},$$

where $f' \in V'_k$ and $f'' \in V''_\ell$ are normalized so that $\langle f', f' \rangle = \langle f'', f'' \rangle = 1$, and $a, b \geq 0$ are not both 0. With this notation, we compute

$$\langle Mf, f \rangle = \langle aM'f' + bNf'', af' \rangle + \langle aN^t f' + bM''f'', bf'' \rangle$$
$$= a^2 \langle M'f', f' \rangle + b^2 \langle M''f'', f'' \rangle + 2ab \, \mathrm{Re}\langle Nf'', f' \rangle.$$

For the non-zero $g \in V$ given by

$$g = \begin{pmatrix} bf' \\ -af'' \end{pmatrix}$$

we have

$$\langle Mg, g \rangle = b^2 \langle M'f', f' \rangle + a^2 \langle M''f'', f'' \rangle - 2ab \, \mathrm{Re}\langle Nf'', f' \rangle,$$

and so, adding and dividing through by $a^2 + b^2 = \langle f, f \rangle = \langle g, g \rangle$, we get

$$R(f) + R(g) = R'(f') + R''(f'').$$

Now $R'(f') \leq \mu'_k$, $R''(f'') \leq \mu''_\ell$, and $R(g) \geq \mu_1$. Therefore $\mu_1 + R(f) \leq \mu'_k + \mu''_\ell$. Maximizing over f yields $\mu_1 + \mu_{k+\ell} \leq \mu'_k + \mu''_\ell$, as desired.

10.16. The upper bound is $\lambda_2(P)$, where P is a path of length δ. Such a path can be found in any tree T of diameter δ. To conclude that $\lambda_2(T) \leq \lambda_2(P)$, it would suffice to prove the following claim: if X' is the graph obtained by removing a pendant vertex from a graph X, then $\lambda_2 \leq \lambda'_2$.

Let X'' be the graph obtained by removing the pendant edge, in other words, it is the disconnected union of X' and a single vertex. Its Laplacian spectrum starts with $\lambda''_1 = \lambda''_2 = 0$, $\lambda''_3 = \lambda'_2$. As in the proof of Theorem 10.14, we have $L'' = L + N$. Weyl's inequality for $k = \ell = 2$ says that $\mu_3(L'') \geq \mu_2(L) + \mu_2(N)$, that is, $\lambda'_2 \geq \lambda_2$ since $\mu_2(N) = 0$. The claim is proved.

Assuming, as usual, that the tree has at least 3 vertices, we get $\delta \geq 2$ and so $\lambda_2(P) \leq 1$. If equality holds then $\delta = 2$, meaning that the tree is a star graph. Conversely, a star graph has $\lambda_2 = 1$ (Exercise 7.13).

Chapter 11

11.3. Consider first a symmetric matrix that is block partitioned as

$$M = \begin{pmatrix} M_1 & & & \\ & M_2 & & \\ & & \ddots & \\ & & & M_k \end{pmatrix},$$

where $M_1, \ldots, M_k$ are symmetric matrices. We show by induction the following inequality, relating the extremal eigenvalues of M with the largest eigenvalues of $M_1, \ldots, M_k$:

$$(k-1)\mu_{\min} + \mu_{\max} \le \mu_{\max}^{(1)} + \cdots + \mu_{\max}^{(k)}. \qquad (*)$$

The base case, $k = 1$, is trivially true. For the induction step, let M' be obtained by deleting from M the rows and columns corresponding to M_k. Then

$$(k-1)\mu_{\min} + \mu_{\max} \le (k-2)\mu'_{\min} + \mu'_{\max} + \mu_{\max}^{(k)} \le \mu_{\max}^{(1)} + \cdots + \mu_{\max}^{(k)}.$$

Indeed, the inequality on the right is the induction hypothesis. The inequality on the left combines two bounds: $\mu_{\min} + \mu_{\max} \le \mu'_{\max} + \mu_{\max}^{(k)}$ by Exercise 10.10, and $\mu_{\min} \le \mu'_{\min}$ by Cauchy's interlacing theorem.

Now let χ denote the chromatic number, and consider a colouring of a graph using χ colours. The chromatic partition of the vertex set defines a block partitioning of the adjacency matrix, in which the diagonal blocks are zero matrices. Then $(*)$ says that $(\chi - 1)\alpha_{\min} + \alpha_{\max} \le 0$.

11.12. (i) The halved cube graph $\frac{1}{2}Q_n$ is the Cayley graph of $G = \{v \in (\mathbb{Z}_2)^n : \sum v_i = 0\}$ with respect to $S = \{e_i + e_j : 1 \le i < j \le n\}$. Now $(\mathbb{Z}_2)^{n-1}$ is isomorphic to G, by $v \mapsto (v, \sum v_i)$, so $\frac{1}{2}Q_n$ is also a Cayley graph of $(\mathbb{Z}_2)^{n-1}$. Specifically, we can pull back S to $S' = \{e_i : 1 \le i \le n-1\} \cup \{e_i + e_j : 1 \le i < j \le n-1\}$. As we have computed in previous exercises, $\frac{1}{2}Q_n$ has $\lambda_2 = 2(n-1)$. So $\frac{1}{2}Q_n$ has isoperimetric constant $n - 1$.

(ii) A decked cube graph $DQ_n(a)$ is, by definition, a Cayley graph of $(\mathbb{Z}_2)^n$, so its isoperimetric constant equals $\lambda_2/2$. The adjacency eigenvalues of $DQ_n(a)$ are given by

$$\alpha_I = \chi_I(a) + \sum_j \chi_I(e_j) = \chi_I(a) + n - 2|I|$$

for $I \subseteq \{1, \ldots, n\}$. Hence the Laplacian eigenvalues are

$$\lambda_I = (n+1) - \alpha_I = 2|I| + 1 - \chi_I(a).$$

The smallest possible non-zero value is $\lambda_I = 2$, achieved when I is a singleton satisfying $\chi_I(a) = 1$. Putting $I = \{i\}$, this means that $a_i = 0$. All but one choices of $a \in (\mathbb{Z}_2)^n$ have a zero entry, so $DQ_n(a)$ has $\lambda_2 = 2$ and isoperimetric constant 1. The only exception is the 'longest' vector $a = e_1 + \cdots + e_n$. In this case, we get $\lambda_2 = 4$ and isoperimetric constant 2.

11.21. While not quite a direct application of Theorem 11.16, the bound can be proved in a similar way. On the one hand, we have

$$\langle A \mathbb{1}_S, \mathbb{1}_S \rangle = e(S, S) = |S| d_{\mathrm{ave}}(S).$$

On the other hand, we write $\mathbb{1}_S = \sum s_k f_k$, where $\{f_k\}$ is an orthonormal basis of adjacency eigenvectors. Here $f_1 = \mathbb{1}/\sqrt{n}$, so $s_1 = \langle \mathbb{1}_S, f_1 \rangle = |S|/\sqrt{n}$. We deduce that

$$\sum_{k \geq 2} |s_k|^2 = \langle \mathbb{1}_S, \mathbb{1}_S \rangle - |s_1|^2 = |S| - \frac{1}{n}|S|^2 = \frac{1}{n}|S|\,|S^c|.$$

As $A\mathbb{1}_S = \sum \alpha_k s_k f_k$, we get

$$\langle A\mathbb{1}_S, \mathbb{1}_S \rangle = \sum \alpha_k |s_k|^2 = d|s_1|^2 + \sum_{k \geq 2} \alpha_k |s_k|^2 = \frac{d}{n}|S|^2 + \sum_{k \geq 2} \alpha_k |s_k|^2.$$

The latter sum can be bounded as

$$\frac{\alpha_n}{n}|S|\,|S^c| = \alpha_n \sum_{k \geq 2} |s_k|^2 \leq \sum_{k \geq 2} \alpha_k |s_k|^2 \leq \alpha_2 \sum_{k \geq 2} |s_k|^2 = \frac{\alpha_2}{n}|S|\,|S^c|.$$

Combining the two expressions for $\langle A\mathbb{1}_S, \mathbb{1}_S \rangle$, and dividing by $|S|$, we reach

$$\frac{d}{n}|S| + \frac{\alpha_n}{n}|S^c| \leq d_{\text{ave}}(S) \leq \frac{d}{n}|S| + \frac{\alpha_2}{n}|S^c|.$$

Now $|S| = \epsilon n$ and $|S^c| = (1 - \epsilon)n$, yielding the desired bound.

11.26. Let u and v be vertices with $\text{dist}(u, v) = \delta$, where δ denotes the diameter. Then $p_\ell(u, v) = 0$ for $\ell < \delta$. We apply the bounds of Theorem 11.24 and Corollary 11.25 to $S = \{u\}$ and $T = \{v\}$.

In the non-bipartite case, we have $|np_\ell(u, v) - d^\ell| \leq (n-1)\alpha^\ell$. Taking $\ell = \delta - 1$, we find that $d^{\delta-1} \leq (n-1)\alpha^{\delta-1}$, that is,

$$\delta - 1 \leq \frac{\log(n-1)}{\log(d/\alpha)}.$$

In the bipartite case, we have $|mp_\ell(u, v) - d^\ell| \leq (m-1)\alpha_2^\ell$. Here we take $\ell = \delta - 2$, and we conclude as above.

Index